Extens...

Mathematics

Tony Gardiner

beta

OXFORD

UNIVERSITY PRESS

UNIVERSITY PRESS

Great Clarendon Street, Oxford OX2 6DP

Oxford University Press is a department of the University of Oxford.
It furthers the University's objective of excellence in research, scholarship,
and education by publishing worldwide in

Oxford   New York

Auckland   Cape Town   Dar es Salaam   Hong Kong   Karachi
Kuala Lumpur   Madrid   Melbourne   Mexico City   Nairobi
New Delhi   Shanghai   Taipei   Toronto

With offices in

Argentina   Austria   Brazil   Chile   Czech Republic   France   Greece
Guatemala   Hungary   Italy   Japan   Poland   Portugal   Singapore
South Korea   Switzerland   Thailand   Turkey   Ukraine   Vietnam

British Library Cataloguing in Publication Data

Data available

ISBN: 978 019 915151 6

10 9 8 7 6 5 4 3

Printed in Great Britain

Contents

Extension

Introduction

This is the second book in a series containing 'extension material' designed for the top 25% or so of lower secondary pupils.

Good quality extension material is not specifically age-related: a good problem appeals to all ages – *as long as it is accessible*. Book *Alpha* was designed to be accessible to the top 25% or so of pupils in the first years of secondary school, limiting assumed prerequisite knowledge to what might be expected at some stage during Year 7 (age 11-12), *but it was in no way restricted to that age group*. Similarly book *Beta* is intended to be accessible to pupils in Year 8 (age 12-13), in that prerequisite knowledge has been limited to what might be routinely taught to the top 25% at some stage during Year 8. But the material is needed by, and can be used effectively with, any pupils in Year 8-10 to whom it is not already familiar – and some of the ideas may be directly relevant to certain older students. (In schools with higher levels of expectation, much of the material can no doubt be used with younger age-groups. However, since much of the material here seeks to encourage pupils not just to grind out answers, but to *think* and to talk about elementary techniques, there are good reasons for hesitating to use the material prematurely, even if at first sight it looks accessible. Nevertheless, teachers are encouraged to adapt and to use sections in ways the author never imagined!) Subsequent volumes are designed for those in Years 9 and 10 *and above*.

The material uses the current English *Frameworks* as a rough guide. But – within this constraint – it seeks to capture and to convey *the essence of elementary mathematics*, rather than to reflect current expectations and norms.

Forty years ago England had a worldwide reputation for the way its schools extended able young mathematicians. This past reputation needs to be interpreted with caution. However, there is no escaping the fact that the structures *currently* in place fail to lay appropriate foundations for the most able 25%. Mathematics retains its perennial appeal – as shown by the huge expansion in mathematics competitions and other extra-curricular opportunities. Yet

◎ very few English Year 9 students achieve at the expected level for able pupils (as indicated by international comparisons)

◎ numbers choosing to study A level mathematics have slumped (despite repeated attempts to make the subject 'more accessible' by removing more demanding material)

◎ our leading universities find it increasingly difficult to identify suitable home-grown applicants who wish to study mathematics.

Mathematics at all levels begins when two or three elementary ideas have to be selected and combined – often in slightly unexpected ways – to solve an elementary but unfamiliar problem. An extension curriculum that embodies this principle is urgently needed – and not just for a small minority of pupils. It should be designed to establish a stronger foundation for a large fraction (around 25%) of each cohort, providing material suitable for *whole classes*, so giving teachers and senior management something to enrich the daily diet for *at least one top set* in every secondary school.

The range of ability between the 75th percentile and the 99th percentile is staggering. Hence the items presented here have been classified into *three levels*:

◎ *Tasters* (numbered **T1** etc.) are meant to be accessible to *all* those in the target group in the sense that they should all be able to tackle the problems and to have a degree of success (though some pupils will inevitably begin to struggle with the later problems, even on *Taster* sets).

◎ *Core* items (numbered **C1** etc.) cover curriculum topics relatively systematically, but may be appropriate only for a subset of those who engage with the *Tasters*. (How big this subset is will inevitably depend on the school and how the pupils have been taught.)

◎ *Extension* items (numbered **E1** etc.) push *Core* ideas slightly further, or venture a little beyond the official curriculum (whilst keeping students' feet firmly on the ground).

Very roughly one might expect *Tasters* to be suitable for 25% of each cohort, *Core* to be suitable for 15-20%, and *Extensions* suitable for 5-10%; however, such figures are highly dependent on teachers' expectations. Complete answers (with some additional discussion) are included in the associated *Teacher's Book*.

Each *Taster* and *Core* section includes a set of problems that is designed to encourage pupils to *develop a specific conceptual insight*, using material that is *closely related to what one finds in most mathematics classrooms*. The problems are to be actively tackled, and thought about – not merely 'answered'. Much of the relevant prerequisite material for these sections should have been covered in ordinary classwork. However, as is natural in a 'series', some *Taster* and *Core* sections in this *second* book develop ideas introduced in the *Taster* and *Core* sections of the *first* book in the series (but never depend on ideas from the *Extension* sections of the first book). *Internal* prerequisites that might otherwise be overlooked are indicated at the top of the relevant section; obvious prerequisites (e.g. where the section title indicates a link with some earlier section – such as *Sequences B*, or *More angles*) are not mentioned explicitly. More general issues and connections are clarified in the associated *Teacher's Book*.

◎ Earlier sections are generally easier (in some sense) than later sections, but there is nothing to stop teachers selecting sections to suit their needs.

◎ The purpose of each section may be missed if pupils are allowed to produce answers in a way that is not in the intended spirit. In particular, the label 'NC' means 'No Calculators'.

◎ Each *Taster* or *Core* section is designed to be used with a complete class.
Every such section begins with **i** a short introductory text and **ii** a *Problem 0*.

  i   The short introductory text in each section must be understood before pupils begin, but teachers are encouraged to decide for themselves how best to structure any necessary review.

  ii **Problem 0** is to be tackled by the whole class. Where this is initially done individually, the results should subsequently be discussed as a group, with contributions and explanations orchestrated by the teacher *to bring out the intended spirit of the section*, and to emphasise any intended approach and layout indicated in the introductory text.

◎ *Problem 0* is *not* meant to be solved by the teacher as a 'worked example'. Rather it is to be solved *by the class* and should be used to bring out – and to correct – misconceptions and errors, so that every member of the class understands how to approach such problems, and so that all pupils emerge from the discussion with a clear idea of what is expected in that section.

◎ *Problem 0* often includes a 'harder' part. This too is to be solved *by the class*, with explanations *from the class*, to ensure that everyone sees how the simple principles being developed can be used to solve harder problems.

◎ Each section requires one or more *specific* insights. Any contributions during the preliminary class discussion that could obscure the intended focus need to be handled carefully. The *way* in which the problems are solved is crucial. Hence the initial class discussion needs to be handled so as to ensure that pupils emerge with the necessary tools to tackle the problems that follow *in the intended spirit*.

Roughly speaking, my goal has been to pursue important themes from the official curriculum in ways that make mathematics more attractive, *exploring simple ideas more deeply* and *bringing out the connections between simple ideas*. The existing curriculum will thereby be mastered in *greater depth*, and *connections* between topics will be systematically established and exploited, counteracting the trend in recent years towards

i   increasing fragmentation

ii superficial coverage

iii lack of fluency

iv failure to develop a clear notion of mathematical proof

all of which contribute to a general failure to engage pupils' mathematical imagination.

Many able pupils are not used to having to work things out the hard way, so when they meet such material, there may be pressure on the teacher to 'help' by giving 'rules' that reduce the pupil's need to struggle. Such premature rules prevent pupils developing their own habit of 'sense making', and deprive them of the satisfaction of achieving the relevant unexpected insight for themselves, and the experience of applying that insight to new problems.

Mathematical mastery requires a considerable amount of repetitive exercising of simple processes. Repetitive practice is needed to achieve the level of *fluency* and *accuracy* that will allow longer chains of calculation to be completed without introducing unanticipated errors due to 'overload'. Such repetition can be a source of considerable pleasure and satisfaction for the learner (and often involves a greater degree of challenge than we acknowledge). Most sections in this series contain lots of exercises to provide this kind of repetition-with-a-purpose.

But it is also important that basic techniques should be routinely used to solve more demanding problems. Hence most sections include a number of problems of a more demanding kind; such problems sometimes appear in a shaded box . These problems are not necessarily harder, or intended for a minority; the shaded box is simply an indication that these problems may require a greater degree of thought or perseverance.

Extension sections provide additional (mostly harder) problems, mainly for those pupils who have already devoured the *Taster* and *Core* sections and who need something more demanding. The *Extension* sections differ slightly from the *Taster* and *Core* sections: whereas the *Taster* and *Core* sections are designed to be used with whole classes, and so have a clear structure, the *Extension* sections may be appropriate only for a minority of those in a top set, so it seems counterproductive to try to prescribe how they should be used. Each section has a theme – but the focus is slightly blurred to keep pupils on their toes. Later problems in each section still tend to be harder than earlier problems, but *Extension* sections are less systematic about highlighting more demanding problems by including them in a shaded box. These sections should therefore be seen as an extra resource in the spirit of *Taster* and *Core* sections, to be used as teachers and pupils see fit.

Elementary mathematics retains its unrivalled potential to appeal to young minds. But many essential techniques and attitudes have recently been downplayed or neglected. This neglect stems in part from pressure on schools to demonstrate 'success' in narrowly focused, and increasingly predictable, central assessments. Unfortunately, tests which are obliged to demonstrate success shy away from those aspects of elementary mathematics that appeal to young minds precisely because they are *accessible, but slightly elusive*. But as observed above, mathematics proper begins when two or three elementary ideas need to be combined to solve an unfamiliar problem. *This series of books provides problem sequences that aim to reinstate this experience on a very simple level.*

◎   The material requires pupils who are willing to struggle, to experience discomfort, and who come to accept this as normal (even tantalising).

◎   In each section *Problem 0* (tackled by the class under the guidance of the teacher) provides the opportunity for any necessary review and preparation.

Pupils may still feel uncomfortable when confronted with the need to work quickly and accurately, or to make sense of unfamiliar-looking problems; but this activity is quintessentially human, and – provided that the demands being made are not unrealistic – the result for ordinary pupils can only be positive. In particular, one can anticipate a fresh flexibility, self-criticism, and self-correction when the same pupils are faced with more straightforward tasks.

Slick sums

NC

Section **T16** of Book *Alpha* showed that *thinking* carefully about sums involving multiplication and division can make calculations much simpler than they seem. For example,

> Calculate the answers to these calculations *in your head* as efficiently as you can.
>
> **a** $(1234 \div 6) \times 12 =$ ___   **c** $((123 \div 4) \times 56) \div 7 =$ ___
>
> **b** $(25 \div 6) \times 78 \quad =$ ___

The above calculations are easier than they look once you realise that the laws of arithmetic allow you to simplify. For example, in part **a** above 'divide by 6 and then multiply by 12' is the same as 'multiply by ___'.

In the above calculations the simple method is easy to spot because the operations that cancel out are carefully positioned next to each other. In this section, you may need to be more alert. Problem **0a** is easy, but think how to work out the other parts efficiently *in your head*.

Problem 0

> **0 a** $30 \div 15 \quad =$ **c** $35 \times 20 \div 14 =$
>
> **b** $18 \times 25 \div 15 =$ **d** $25 \times 21 \div 75 =$

The whole point here is that you should look for ways of cancelling that reduce the need to work with fractions: in problem **0b**

$$18 \times 25 \div 15 = (\underline{\ \ } \times 3) \times (\underline{\ \ } \times 5) \div (3 \times 5) = \underline{\ \ } .$$

Work out the answers to these problems efficiently *in your head*.

1 $70 \div 14$	**5** $49 \times 22 \div 14$	**9** $56 \times 15 \div 24$
2 $45 \times 10 \div 9$	**6** $72 \times 34 \div 51$	**10** $117 \times 14 \div 18$
3 $63 \times 11 \div 7$	**7** $120 \times 28 \div 21$	
4 $54 \times 20 \div 12$	**8** $81 \times 14 \div 18$	

> **11** Work out the answers to these problems efficiently *in your head*.
>
> **a** $111 \times 23 \div 37$ **c** $(8 \div 16) \times 24) \div 32$
>
> **b** $126 \times 49 \div 42$ **d** $((((2 \div 4) \times 8) \div 16) \times 32) \div 64$

T2 Eyeing the dots

This exercise prepares the way for the more formal approach to parallel lines in section C2. The intention is for pupils to *grapple* with the meaning of the words *parallel* and *perpendicular* in a concrete setting, without being given half-understood rules.

Problem 0

> **0** Take a sheet of 1 cm square dotty paper.
>
> **a** Mark points *A*, *B* exactly as shown on the right.
> Draw accurately the line *AB*, extending it beyond *A* and beyond *B*.
> Mark the point *X* exactly as shown in the diagram.
>
> **b** Draw the exact line through the point *X* that is parallel to *AB*.
>
> **c** Draw the exact line through the point *X* that is perpendicular to *AB*.

Going from *A* to *B* involves moving '___ steps along and ___ step up', so in part **b** it is natural to do the same starting from *X*. Drawing the *e**e**i*u*a* to *AB* in part **c** may well provoke more discussion!

Along and *up* are informal versions of 'in the (positive) *x*-direction' and 'in the (positive) *y*-direction': the motion from *A* to *B* has already been naturally imagined in terms of these two components.
When you turn through a right angle (say to the left),
    the '*x*-direction' changes to 'the (positive) ___ direction',
    the '*y*-direction' changes to 'the (negative) ___ direction',
and the motion 'along 2 and up 1' *a*a**e* to *AB* becomes 'u* 2 and a*o** −1' (and is now *e**e**i*u*a* to *AB*).

1 Take a sheet of 1 cm square dotty paper.

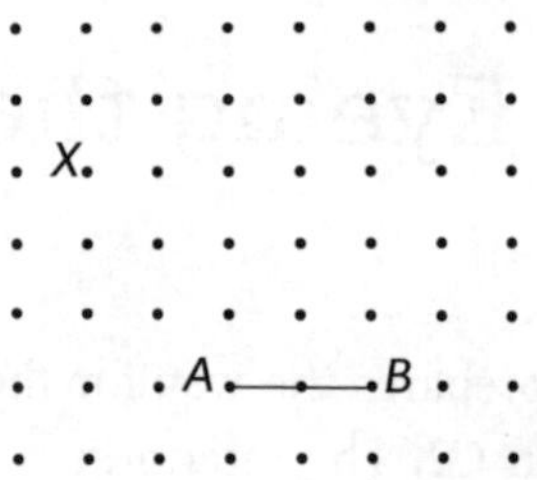

   a Mark points *A*, *B* exactly as shown on the right.
      Draw accurately the line *AB*, extending it
      beyond *A* and beyond *B*.
      Mark the point *X* exactly as shown here.

   b Draw the exact line through the point *X*
      that is parallel to *AB*.

   c Draw the exact line through the point *X* that
      is perpendicular to *AB*.

2 Take a sheet of 1 cm square dotty paper.

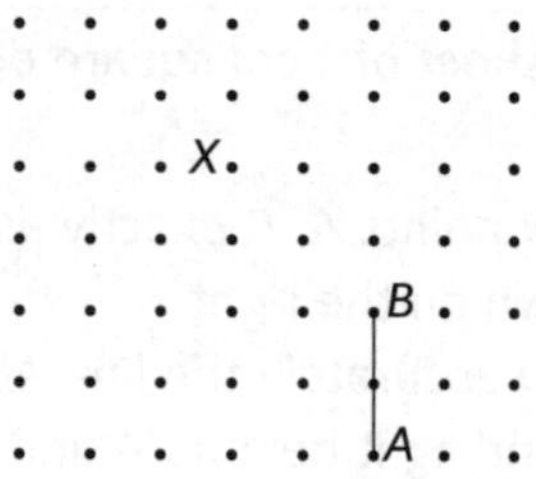

   a Mark points *A*, *B* exactly as shown on the right.
      Draw accurately the line *AB*, extending it
      beyond *A* and beyond *B*.
      Mark the point *X* exactly as shown here.

   b Draw the exact line through the point *X* that
      is parallel to *AB*.

   c Draw the exact line through the point *X* that
      is perpendicular to *AB*.

3 Take a sheet of 1 cm square dotty paper.
   Mark points *A*, *B* exactly as shown on the right.
   Draw accurately the line *AB*, extending it beyond
   A and beyond *B*.
   Mark the points *X*, *Y*, *Z* exactly as shown here.

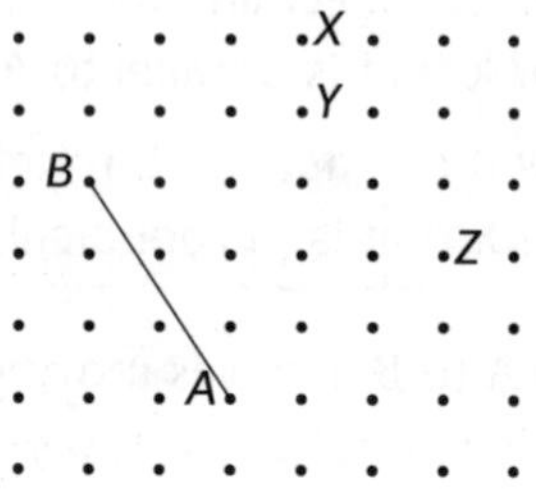

   a i Draw the exact line through the point *X* that is
      parallel to *AB*.

     ii Draw the exact line through *X* that is perpendicular to *AB*.

   b i Draw the exact line through the point *Y* that is parallel to *AB*.

     ii Draw the exact line through the point *Y* that is perpendicular
      to *AB*.

   c i Draw the exact line through the point *Z* that is parallel to *AB*.

     ii Draw the exact line through the point *Z* that is perpendicular
      to *AB*.

 **T3** ## Word sums *A*

T3 Word sums *A* NC

In a *word sum* each letter stands for one of the digits 0–9. Different letters stand for different digits, and each letter stands for the same digit each time it occurs. None of the integers in a word sum starts with a 0.

Your job is to work out which digits the different letters could stand for (if possible using logic rather than guesswork).

A given word sum may be impossible (in which case you have to explain why it cannot have a solution), *or* it may have just one solution (in which case you should try to find that solution and prove that it is the only one), *or* it may have several solutions (in which case you might like to think how many solutions there are, but you should start by finding one that works).

Problem 0

0 Find one solution to this word sum.   O N E
                 + O N E
                   T W O

For each of the word sums in problems 1–4 find one solution that works.

1   T W O
      + T W O
      F O U R

3   O N E
       + F O U R
        F I V E

2   F O U R
      + F O U R
      E I G H T

4   F O U R
      + F I V E
      N I N E

5 a Can you work out what T has   T H I S
     to be in this word sum?   + I S
                                   H A R D
 	
   b Try to find all the possible solutions to the word sum.

 **T4** Mental arithmetic

As you begin to understand more about the structure of arithmetic, all sorts of calculations become easier. For example

◎ you can change the order in which terms are added or subtracted, and so group them to make easy *subtotals*

$127 + 371 - 128 = 371 + (127 - 128) =$ ___
$127 + 369 + 273 = (127 + 273) + 369 =$ ___

◎ you can group together products which have a *common factor*.

$23 \times 49 + 23 \times 11 = 23 \times$ ___ $=$ ___

◎ you can cancel factors to avoid first multiplying and then dividing by the same number

$16 \times 15 \div 24 =$ ___

◎ you can multiply by 10 (or 100, or ___) to change a multiplication or division involving decimals into one involving integers (as long as you remember to divide by 10, or 100, or ... at the end)

$2.1 \times 25 = ($ ___ $\times 25) \div 10 =$ ___ $\div 10 =$ ___
$2.1 \div 30 = ($ ___ $\div 30) \div 10 = (7 \div 10) \div 10 =$ ___

Problem 0

0 a $2.1 \times 25 = ($ ___ $\times 25) \div 10 =$ ___ $\div 10 =$

b $2.1 \div 30 = ($ ___ $\div 30) \div 10 = ($ ___ $\div 10) \div 10 =$

c $44 \times \frac{3}{14} + 13 \times \frac{3}{7} = ($ ___ $+$ ___ $) \times$ ___ $=$

1 $224 - 450 + 225 =$

2 $15 \times 11 + 9 \times 15 =$ ___ $\times$ ___
$=$

3 $\frac{3}{5} \times \frac{5}{8}$ $=$

4 $17 \times \frac{2}{5} + 17 \times \frac{3}{5} =$ ___ $\times ($ ___ $+$ ___ $)$
$=$

5 $24.8 \div 8$ $=$

6 $10.8 \div 0.9$ $=$

7 12×1.1 $=$

8 $\frac{3}{5} \times \frac{15}{8}$ $=$

9 $\frac{9}{11} \div \frac{3}{11}$ $=$

10 $\frac{7}{9} \times \frac{3}{7}$ $=$

11 13×0.13 $=$

12 1.2×11 $=$

13 $\frac{39}{18} \div \frac{26}{15}$ $=$

14 12×3.1 $=$

15 21×2.1 $=$

16 $12.1 \div 8.8 =$

T5 Analogue angles NC

Problem 0

> **0 a** What angle does the minute hand turn through between 2:30 and 3:30?
>
> **b** What angle does the hour hand turn through between 2:30 and 3:30?
>
> **c** What is the angle between the two hands of a clock at 2:30?

1 a What angle does the minute hand turn through between 2:40 and 3:40?

b What angle does the hour hand turn through between 2:40 and 3:40?

2 a What angle does the minute hand turn through between 3:40 and 4:20?

b What angle does the hour hand turn through between 3:40 and 4:20?

3 What is the angle between the two hands of a clock

    a at 3:30?   **c** at 7:30?   **e** at 7:40?

    b at 12:20?   **d** at 4:20?   **f** at 8:40?

4 What is the angle between the two hands of a clock

    a at 4:10?   **c** at 3:50?   **e** at 8:45?

    b at 9:10?   **d** at 6:50?   **f** at 7:45?

5 a What angle does the minute hand turn through between 1:50 and 5:10?

b What angle does the hour hand turn through between 1:50 and 5:10?

6 What is the angle between the two hands of a clock at 3:20? Give another time when the angle between the hands is the same.

7 What is the angle between the two hands of a clock at 4:30? Give another time when the angle between the hands is the same.

8 What is the angle between the two hands of a clock at 11:40?
Give another time when the angle between the hands
is the same.

9 What is the angle between the two hands of a clock at 3:40?
Give another time when the angle between the hands is
the same.

10 What is the angle between the two hands of a clock at 8:30?
Give another time when the angle between the hands is
the same.

11 What is the angle between the two hands of a clock at 6:15?
Give another time when the angle between the hands is
the same.

12 What is the angle between the two hands of a clock at 9:15?
Give another time when the angle between the hands is
the same.

13 What is the angle between the two hands of a clock at 4:15?
Give another time when the angle between the hands is
the same.

14 What is the angle between the two hands of a clock at 6:10?
Give another time when the angle between the hands is
the same.

15 What is the angle between the two hands of a clock at 2:25?
Give another time when the angle between the hands is
the same.

16 What is the angle between the two hands of a clock at 6 pm?
Give another time other than 6 am when the angle between the
hands is the same.

T6 Missing digits NC

Given any two starting numbers, you should be able, *quickly* and *reliably*, and without a calculator, to add one to the other, to subtract one from the other, to multiply one by the other, or to divide one by the other.

The logic behind the arithmetical algorithms for addition, subtraction, multiplication and division leads *from* the given starting numbers *to* the answer. But if you understand what is really going on, and are willing to *think*, you should be able to *work backwards* and fill in the missing digits.

Problem 0

0 Work out the missing digits in this addition. Explain why there is only one solution.	``` * 5\n+ *\n------\n* * 3```

1 Work out the missing digits in this addition. Explain why there is only one solution.
```
  * 3
+ 2 *
-----
* 1 0
```

2 Find all solutions to this multiplication and prove that you have found them all.
```
  * 4
×   *
-----
* 8 6
```

3 Use the digits 1, 2, 3, 4, 5 once each to complete this multiplication. Explain why there is only one solution.
```
* *
× *
---
* *
```

4 Use the digits 3, 4, 5, 6, 7 once each to complete this addition. Explain why there is essentially only one solution.
```
  * *
+ * 
-----
* *
```

5 Find all the solutions to this multiplication and prove that you have found them all.
```
  * 7
×   *
-----
2 * 8
```

6 Find all solutions to this multiplication and prove that you have found them all.
```
  * 6
×   *
-----
3 * 8
```

T7 Intelligent grouping

NC

We all know that 7 *eights* and 3 *eights* make 10 *eights* (or 80); that is,

$(7 \times 8) + (3 \times 8) = (7 + 3) \times 8 = 10 \times 8 = 80.$

This works just as well with negative numbers.

$(7 \times -8) + (3 \times -8) = (7 + 3) \times (-8) = 10 \times (-8) = \underline{\quad}$

$(7 \times -8) - (3 \times -8) = (7 - 3) \times (-8) = 4 \times (-8) = \underline{\quad}.$

Use this idea to answer each question quickly *in your head* (that is, *without* working out the two terms separately and then adding).

Problem 0

0 **a** **i** $14 \times (-7) + (6 \times (-7)) = \underline{\quad} \times (-7) =$

      ii $14 \times (-7) - (6 \times (-7)) = \underline{\quad} \times (-7) =$

  b **i** $(-4) \times 7 + 7 \times 6 = \underline{\quad} \times 7 =$ **ii** $(-4) \times 7 - 6 \times 7 =$

  c **i** $14 \times 7 + 7 \times (-6) =$ **ii** $14 \times 7 - (-6) \times 7 =$

  d $14 \times 5 + 14 \times (-5) =$

  e $11 \times (-15) + 33 \times 5 =$

1 $(15 \times -7) + (5 \times -7) = \underline{\quad} \times (-7) =$ **10** $(47 \times -3) - (43 \times -3) =$

2 $(15 \times -7) - (5 \times -7) = \underline{\quad} \times (-7) =$ **11** $29 \times 14 + (-4) \times 29 =$

3 $(12 \times -3) + (8 \times -3) = \underline{\quad} \times (-3) =$ **12** $9 \times 17 + 9 \times (-8) =$

4 $(12 \times -3) - (8 \times -3) =$ **13** $12 \times (-18) - (-12) \times 18 =$

5 $(12 \times 3) + (-8 \times 3) = \underline{\quad} \times 3 =$ **14** $37 \times 16 - 37 \times (-4) =$

6 $(12 \times 3) - (-8 \times 3) = \underline{\quad} \times 3 =$ **15** $23 \times 18 + (-3) \times 18 =$

7 $17 \times 13 + (-7) \times 13 =$ **16** $23 \times 18 + (-27) \times 2 =$

8 $(47 \times -3) + (43 \times -3) = \underline{\quad} \times (-3) =$ **17** $34 \times (-9) + 17 \times 18 =$

9 $(47 \times -3) - (-3 \times -3) = \underline{\quad} \times (-3) =$ **18** $(-12) \times 36 - 24 \times (-18) =$

19 **a** $17 \times (-33)) + 3 \times (-33) =$ **c** $(-23) \times 27 - (-3) \times 27 =$

     b $16 \times (-42) - (-42) \times 6 =$

20 Evaluate $(37 \times 458) + (63 \times 458)$ and divide the answer by 8.

T8 Enlargement A

Suppose you are given a geometrical figure. If all *horizontal* and *vertical* lengths are *doubled* (say), you may think it is obvious that all other lengths should also double. But this is not at all obvious! In Section C27 you will have the chance to explain why it is in fact true; meanwhile it is worth getting hands-on experience of what seems to happen.

Problem 0

0 **a** Take a sheet of 1 cm square dotty paper and copy this figure leaving two thirds of the page free. Measure the distance in your copy from the point *X* (base of the right ear) to the point *Y* (left-hand corner of the mouth).

b Now make a '2 × enlargement' of your figure – with the distance between the ears *A′B′* = 4 cm instead of *AB* = 2 cm. Think before measuring what the distance from *X′* to *Y′* should be in your enlargement. Then measure to check.

1 **a** Copy this 'face' onto 1 cm square dotty paper. Measure the distance on your copy from the top of the right-hand hair spike at *A* to the tip of the nose at *C*.

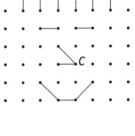

b Make a second drawing of the same 'face', but this time with *A′B′* = 2 cm instead of *AB* = 1 cm. What do you expect the distance in your '2 × enlargement' to be from the top of the right-hand hair spike at *A′* to the tip of the nose at *C′*? Measure *A′C′* to check.

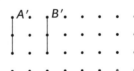

2 a Copy this 'face' onto 1 cm square dotty paper.
Measure the distance *AZ* on your copy from *A*
(right end of the right eyebrow) to *Z* (left-hand
corner of the mouth).

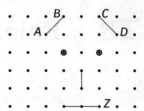

b Make a second drawing of the same 'face',
but with *B'C'* = 6 cm instead of *BC* = 2 cm.
What do you expect the distance *A'Z'* in
your '3 × enlargement' to be from the
right-hand end of the right eyebrow at *A'*
to the left corner of the mouth at *Z'*?
Measure *A'Z'* to check.

T9   Sequences   NC

A *sequence* is a way of presenting lots of information in a single list. The *terms* of the sequence have to be *defined* in some way: they may count something, or they may be specified by some recipe – such as
    'always add two to the previous term to get the next term'.

Problem 0

> **0 a** A sequence is defined by the rule:
>   'always add 2 to the previous term to get the next term'.
>   If the first term is 3, write out the first ten terms.
>
> **b** Suppose you know that a sequence begins 1, 2, 3, ...
>
>   **i** What do you expect the next term to be (assuming that the sequence obeys the simplest possible rule)?
>   Express your rule for finding the next term in words.
>
>   **ii** What do you expect the 10th term in this sequence to be?

There are two quite different ways of defining the terms of a sequence.

◎ The first way is with a *term-to-term* rule that tells you how to work out the next term (see problem **0a**).

A term-to-term rule is easy to use, but it has the disadvantage that to work out the 50th term you must first work out the previous 49 terms.

◎ The second way is with a *position-to-term* rule which describes how each term of the sequence depends on its position in the sequence, that is, it explains directly
    how the 5th term can be calculated directly from the number 5,
    how the 50th term can be calculated directly from the number 50,
    and in general how the number n determines the value of the nth term.

A position-to-term rule may be a *verbal description*, such as
'the nth term is the number of triangles in the nth figure of a given kind';
that is, the 5th term is 'the number of triangles in the 5th figure', the 50th term is 'the number of triangles in the 50th figure', and so on.

A position-to-term rule may also be given as a *formula*, such as
    'the nth term is given by the formula $3n + 1$', that is,
    the 1st term is obtained by substituting $n = 1$ in the formula $3n + 1$
    the 5th term is obtained by substituting $n = 5$ in the formula $3n + 1$
    the 50th term is obtained by substituting $n = 50$ in the formula $3n + 1$, etc.

Problem 0

> **0 b** Suppose you know that a sequence begins
>
>   1, 2, 3, . . .
>
> **iii** What do you expect the nth term to be? Express your rule by giving a *formula* for the nth term.
>
> **c** Suppose you know that a sequence begins
>
>   2, 3, 5, . . .
>
> **i** What might you expect the next term to be (assuming that the sequence is determined by a rule that is as simple as possible)? Express your rule in words.
>
> **ii** What do you expect the 10th term in this sequence to be?
>
> **iii** What do you expect the nth term to be?

If all you know is the first few terms of a sequence, there is no way to be sure how it continues: you cannot hope to identify even a very well-behaved sequence from its first *three* terms. For example, the *On-line Encyclopedia of Integer Sequences* lists 10 980 well-known sequences in mathematics that begin '1, 2, 3, . . .', and 4003 well-known sequences that begin '2, 3, 5, . . .'. Nevertheless, when you only know the first few terms of a sequence, it is natural, and a good exercise, to look for the *simplest* rule that could generate the terms you already know.

There is an obvious candidate that everyone would accept as the simplest possible sequence beginning 1, 2, 3, . . ., so in problem **0b** you probably found a rule for the next term, and even a formula for the nth term.

The same is less likely to be true for the example '2, 3, 5, . . .' in problem **0c**. How you expect this sequence to continue will depend on where you think it comes from. If challenged to 'Guess my rule', a mathematician would be inclined to suspect that this was the sequence of **i**e **u**e** in which case the next term would be 7. On the other hand a secondary pupil might be more likely to think of a term-to-term rule such as 'a** o*e, a** **o' and so might guess that the next term is ___ (given by "a** ***ee"). In either case, you should manage to give a rule in words for finding the next term, and should probably be able to find the 10th term. But you will have difficulty giving a *formula* for the nth term.

This highlights the general fact that it may be relatively easy to find a term-to-term rule for a sequence, but is often much harder to discover a formula for the nth term – which is what you really need in order to do serious mathematical calculations.

In this section your main job is to concentrate on seeing how to spot a likely term-to-term rule.

1 You are told the first four terms of a sequence. In each case decide what you expect the next term to be (assuming that the sequence obeys the simplest possible rule).
Express in words the term-to-term rule you use to obtain the next term.

a 1, 2, 4, 8, . . .   g 2, 4, 8, 16, . . .

b 1, 3, 5, 7, . . .   h 2, 4, 7, 11, . . .

c 1, 3, 6, 10, . . .   i 3, 6, 9, 12, . . .

d 1, 3, 7, 15, . . .   j 4, 7, 10, 13, . . .

e 1, 3, 9, 27, . . .   k 2, 5, 8, 11, . . .

f 2, 4, 6, 8, . . .   l 4, 8, 12, 16, . . .

2 Suppose that you have a plentiful supply of 1p and 2p stamps.

a There is just one way to make up 1p.
How many ways are there to make up 2p worth of stamps?

b How many ways are there to make up 3p?

c How many ways are there to make up 4p?

d Make a table to show how many ways there are to make up each amount up to 10p.

Amount made up	0p	1p	2p	3p	4p	5p	6p	7p	8p	9p	10p
Number of ways	1										

e Express in words the term-to-term rule for finding the next term in the bottom row.

f Give a position-to-term recipe for finding the nth term directly (that is, for predicting the exact number of ways of making up n using only 1s and 2s).
Explain why your position-to-term recipe really does count what you claim it counts.

T10 Powers

NC

This section is an exercise in recognising and writing integers as powers.

Our *base 10* numeral system represents all positive integers by combining the ten *digits* 0–9, and *place value* based on powers of 10.

Counting from the right, each 'place' corresponds to the next power of 10.

ten thousands	thousands	hundreds	tens	units
$10\,000 = 10^4$,	$1000 = 10^3$,	$100 = 10^2$,	$10 = 10^1$,	$1 = 10^?$

This suggests that '$1 = 10^0$'. To see why this makes sense, look at

$$10^2 \times 10^3 = (10 \times 10) \times (10 \times 10 \times 10)$$
$$= 10^5 = 10^{2+3}$$

For the same reason, when m and n are positive integers, the product of
10^m (10 multiplied by itself m times) and
10^n (10 multiplied by itself n times)
is equal to
'10 multiplied by itself $m + n$ times',
$$\therefore 10^m \times 10^n = 10^{m+n}$$

For this calculation rule to be valid when $n = 0$, you need
$$10^1 \times 10^0 = 10^{1+0} = 10^1$$
and for this you have to take $10^0 = 1$.

◎ The *units* digit counts the number of 1s ($1 = 10^0$) in the 0th position.

◎ The *tens* digit counts the number of 10s ($10 = 10^1$) in the 1st position.

◎ The *hundreds* digit counts the number of 100s ($100 = 10^2$) in the 2nd position. And so on.

It is often important to think in terms of *powers*, so that

8 is written as 2^3
16 is written as 4^2, or as 2^4
81 is written as 9^2, or as 3^4
144 is written as 12^2
625 is written as 25^2, or as 5^4, and
$1\,000\,000$ is written as 10^6.

Complete each of the equations below by writing the missing number as the *highest possible* power (that is, with the largest possible exponent, so $16 = 2^4$, not 4^2). Some of the resulting equations are accidents, but others are instances of a more general result.

Problem 0

0 a $3^2 + 4^2 =$

  b $2^0 + 2^1 + 2^2 = \underline{} - 1$

  c $8^3 + 6^3 = \underline{} - 1^3$

  d $2^2 + 4^2 + 5^2 + 6^2 =$

1 $6^2 + 8^2 =$

2 $5^2 + 12^2 =$

3 $6^2 - 5^2 + 4^2 =$

4 $3^3 + 4^2 + 5^1 + 6^0 =$

5 $8^2 - 7^2 = \underline{} - 1^4$

6 $9^2 + 8^2 = \underline{} + 1^2$

7 $8^3 - 7^3 =$

8 $9^3 - 8^3 = \underline{} + 1^3$

9 $5^3 - 4^3 + 3^3 - 2^3 + 1^3 =$

10 $5^3 + 4^3 + 2^3 - 1^3 =$

11 $1^3 + 2^3 + 3^3 =$

12 $1^3 + 2^3 + 3^3 + 4^3 =$

13 $1^3 - 2^2 + 3^1 =$

14 $1^5 - 2^4 + 3^3 - 4^2 + 5^1 =$

15 $7^3 - 6^3 = \underline{} - 1^7$

16 $2^0 + 2^1 + 2^2 + 2^3 + 2^4 = \underline{} - 1$

17 $1^3 + 2^3 + 3^3 + 4^3 + 5^3 + 6^3 + 7^3 + 8^3 =$

18 $(3^3 + 3^2 + 3^1 + 3^0)(3^1 - 3^0) = \underline{} - 1$

19 $1^1 + 2^2 + 3^3 =$

20 $6^3 - 5^3 + 4^3 - 3^3 =$

21 $9^3 + 10^3 = \underline{} + 1^3$

22 $3^3 + 4^3 + 5^3 =$

T11 Drawing conclusions A: Isosceles triangles

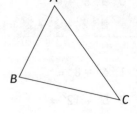

A triangle is more than just a shape – it is a *labelled* shape!
The order of the vertices matters.
A labelled triangle ABC has six 'parts':

◎ three *sides* (AB, BC, CA), and

◎ three *angles* (the angle $\angle CAB$ at the vertex A, the angle $\angle ABC$ at the vertex B, and the angle $\angle BCA$ at the vertex C).

You should know that:
     'a triangle ABC is *isosceles* (with *base* BC and *apex* A) if AB = AC'.

The two equal sides AB, AC are called the *legs* of the isosceles triangle (because the word 'iso-sceles' comes from the Greek for 'equal-legs': 'sceles' should remind you of the ordinary English word ∗∗e∗e∗o∗).

Two triangles $\triangle ABC$ and $\triangle A'B'C'$ are called *congruent* if they are 'equal in all respects' – that is, the six parts of one (labelled) triangle match the corresponding six parts of the other (labelled) triangle:

$$AB = A'B', \qquad BC = B'C', \qquad CA = C'A';$$
$$\angle ABC = \angle A'B'C', \quad \angle BCA = \angle B'C'A', \quad \angle CAB = \angle C'A'B'.$$

Problem 0

---

0 Take a sheet of A4 paper.

   i   Draw (as accurately as you can) a line segment AB with AB = 12 cm. Make sure that you label the two endpoints A and B.

   ii Use a protractor to construct – and to draw in lightly – a line AX with $\angle BAX = 54°$. Use a ruler to mark (as accurately as you can) the point C on the line AX with AC =12 cm.

   iii Now AB = AC = 12 cm, so $\triangle ABC$ is i∗o∗∗e∗e∗ (with base BC and $\angle BAC = 54°$).

   iv Draw triangle ABC to stand out clearly.
       Measure $\angle ABC$ and $\angle ACB$. What do you notice?

The definition of isosceles states that triangle ABC is 'isosceles with base BC' if 'AB = AC'. This says nothing about *angles*! However, it is an important fact that 'the *base angles* of an isosceles triangle *are always equal*'.

This fact that
'the base angles of any isosceles triangle are equal'
is one of the most useful results in elementary geometry.

1 a In an isosceles triangle ABC with $AB = AC$ the apex angle
$\angle BAC = 40°$.
Draw a sketch of $\triangle ABC$ and mark the given information on
your sketch. Find the other two angles in the triangle.

 b In an isosceles triangle ABC with $AB = AC$ the base angle
$\angle ABC = 55°$.
Draw a sketch of $\triangle ABC$ and mark the given information on
your sketch. Find the other two angles in the triangle.

 c In an isosceles triangle, the apex angle is three times as large
as a base angle. Draw a sketch of $\triangle ABC$ and mark the given
information on your sketch. Find all three angles in the triangle.

 d In an isosceles triangle, the apex angle is eight times as
large as a base angle. Draw a sketch and mark the given
information on your sketch. Find all three angles in the triangle.

 e In an isosceles triangle, the sizes of the apex angle and
a base angle are in the ratio 4 : 3. Draw a sketch and mark
the given information on your sketch. Find all three angles.

In each of the remaining problems, draw a sketch and mark the given
information on your sketch before trying to solve the problem.

2 a $ABCD$ is a square. P is a point inside the square such that
$\triangle PCD$ is an equilateral triangle. Calculate $\angle PAB$, $\angle APB$.

 b $ABCD$ is a square. P is a point outside the square such that
$\triangle PCD$ is an equilateral triangle. Calculate $\angle PAB$, $\angle APB$.

3 a Draw a line segment BD of length 24 cm. Mark points X, Y on BD
such that $BX = DY = 13$ cm. Use compasses to draw the circle with
centre B passing through X and the circle with centre D passing
through Y; let these two circles meet at A. Mark the mid-point M of BD.
Measure AM. In what way is the length of AM slightly surprising?

 b Extend AM to the point C such that $AM = MC$. Measure BC, DC.
What does this suggest about the quadrilateral $ABCD$?

A quadrilateral $ABCD$ with $AB = BC = CD = DA$ is called a **rhombus**.

4 a Let $ABCD$ be a rhombus with $\angle DAB = 40°$.

 i Calculate the sizes of $\angle ABD$, $\angle ADB$.

 ii Explain why $\angle BAC = \angle BCA$ and $\angle DAC = \angle DCA$. Hence show
that $\angle BCD = \angle BAD$.

 iii Calculate $\angle CBD$, $\angle CDB$. Hence show that $\angle ABC = \angle ADC$.

b Let *ABCD* be a rhombus with ∠*DAB* = x°.

  i Calculate the sizes of ∠*ABD*, ∠*ADB*.

  ii Explain why ∠*BAC* = ∠*BCA* and ∠*DAC* = ∠*DCA*.
  Hence show that ∠*BCD* = ∠*BAD*.

  iii Calculate ∠*CBD*, ∠*CDB*. Hence show that ∠*ABC* = ∠*ADC*.

A quadrilateral *ABCD* with AB = AD and CB = CD is called a **kite**.

5 Let *ABCD* be a kite with AB = AD, CB = CD.
Prove that ∠*ADC* = ∠*ABC*.

6 A circle has centre *O* and diameter *AB*. *X* is a point on the circumference.

  a Suppose ∠*BAX* = 70°. Calculate ∠*AOX*, ∠*BOX*, ∠*OXB*, ∠*AXB*.

  b Suppose ∠*BAX* = x°. Calculate ∠*AOX*, ∠*BOX*, ∠*OXB*, ∠*AXB* in terms of *x*.
  What is special about the triangle *AXB*?

7 Given a line segment *OA*, let the circle with centre *O* and passing through the point *A* meet the circle with centre *A* passing through the point *O* at *B* and *F*.

  a Calculate ∠*BAO*.

  b Let *AO* produced meet the first circle again at *X*.
  Calculate ∠*AXB*.

A quadrilateral *ABCD* with four right angles is called a **rectangle**.

8 Let *AC* be a diameter of a circle with centre *O*. Let *B* be a third point on the circumference of the circle, and let *BO* produced meet the circle again at *D*.
Prove that *ABCD* is a rectangle.

9 *ABCDE* is a regular pentagon inscribed in a circle with centre *O*.

  a How many different 'congruence classes' (that is, different sizes and shapes) of isosceles triangles are formed by the six points *A*, *B*, *C*, *D*, *E*, *O*? (For example: △*ABC* and △*BCD* are 'equal in all respects', so belong to the same 'congruence class'.)

  b How many isosceles triangles are there in each congruence class?

10 *O* is the centre of the circle and *AOBP* is a straight line.
RQP is also a straight line. If *PQ* is equal to the radius of the circle, prove that ∠*AOR* = 3 × ∠*BOQ*.

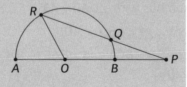

T12 Change of units   NC

Problem 0

> **0 a** How many square millimetres are there in 1 square metre?
>
> **b** What does a cubic metre of water weigh?

1 Which person is heavier: one who weighs 75 kg or one who weighs 12 stone?

2 A typist can type 50 words per minute. How long will he take to type 12 pages with 300 words per page?

3 The rectangular field at the rear of my house measures 120 m by 85 m. What is its area in hectares?

4 Which is more expensive: half a litre of beer for €3.40 or a pint for £2.45?

5 Quince, quance and quonce are three types of fruit found in *The Land Beyond the Mountain*. If 3 quince weigh the same as 4 quance, and 5 quance weigh the same as 6 quonce, how many quonce weigh the same as 5 quince?

6 a What is 60 yards to the nearest metre? What is 35 yards to the nearest metre?

b What is 1 inch in centimetres (to 1 decimal place)?

c Yesterday a good inch of rain fell on my back garden. If the garden is rectangular and measures 60 yards by 35 yards, what was the total weight of water that fell on it?

7 I am 50 years, 50 months, 50 weeks and 50 days old. How old am I to the nearest month?

8 Which car is more economical: one that averages 40 miles to the gallon, or one that uses 8 litres of petrol per 100 km?

9 It is 125 miles from London to Bristol. If £1 coins were laid edge to edge along the side of the road all the way from London to Bristol, how much would the line be worth?

10 Which is longer: **a** 1 000 000 seconds, or 10 days?

b 1 000 000 minutes, or 100 weeks?

c 1 000 000 hours, or 100 years?

11 4! is sometimes written as shorthand for $4 \times 3 \times 2 \times 1$.

a How long is 4! hours?   **c** How long is 6! hours?

b How long is 5! minutes?   **d** How many weeks equal 7! minutes?

e If Fergus averages 8! furlongs per fortnight, what is that in miles per hour?

f How long is 10! seconds?

TASTER

T13 Counting the ways

Problem 0

> **0 a** The mouse can smell cheese through the two partitions – one with holes at *A* and *B*, and one with holes at *X*, *Y* and *Z*. How many different routes are there for the mouse to find his way through the two partitions to get the cheese?
>
> **b** What if there were 3 holes in the first partition and 5 holes in the second partition?

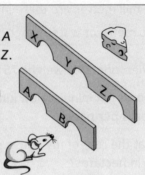

Questions that ask 'How many?' involve *counting*. But this needs to be *intelligent* counting – not counting on your fingers, or 'counting by marking each route with a different coloured felt-tip pen'! To solve problem **0** properly you need an insight that will work just as well if there are 9 holes in the first partition and 99 holes in the second.

One approach is to think about how you could make a *systematic* list of *all* possible routes. This is a much better idea than simply trying to count the routes one at a time – especially if you focus on the question of *how to make sure the list is complete* when, for example, there are 9 holes and 99 holes instead of just 2 holes and 3 holes.

Each route involves choosing *one* hole in the first partition (A or B), and *one* hole in the second partition (*X*, or *Y*, or *Z*). So each route can be summarised by a *pair* of letters, for example
'first A, then X', or just 'AX' for short.

The number of different routes with first hole A = ___;
and the number of different routes with first hole B = ___.
Before adding these two *subtotals* to get the *total number of routes*,
it is worth clarifying *why* the two sub-totals are *equal*.
A route with first hole A can be extended via X, via Y, or via Z
and the same is true for a route with first hole B.
So each sub-total counts the possible second coordinates, X, Y, Z.

It is therefore better to think of the total as '2 lots of 3', or as 2 × 3: the 2 tells us that there are 2 possible first holes, and the 3 tells us that there are 3 possible second holes.
So each route corresponds to one of the dots in the array here.

AZ •   BZ •

AY •   BY •

AX •   BX •

You should now see how to write the answer to problem **0b** – as a product ___ × ___.

The problems below are all like problem **0** – provided you look at them in the right way.

1 a On a weekend break I take two different pairs of shorts and three different T-shirts. How many different combinations of T-shirts and shorts do I have to choose from?

b On the same trip, my wife takes two skirts and three blouses. How many different combinations can she make?
What if she takes three skirts and five blouses?

2 I toss a coin twice.
How many different sequences 'first outcome, second outcome' are possible (such as 'Tails, Heads' or just 'T, H')?

3 I roll an ordinary dice twice.
How many different sequences 'first outcome, second outcome' are possible (such as '3, 6')?

4 Five pupils are standing for election as Form Captain and Vice Captain; three are standing for election as Captain and two are standing for election as Vice Captain.
How many possible final pairings 'Captain, Vice Captain' are there?

5 a A restaurant offers a standard two-course menu with three choices for starter and four choices for the main course.
How many different two-course meals can be made from such a menu?

b Another restaurant boasts that its standard two-course menu allows '121 different combinations'.
What can you conclude about the number of different starters and the number of different main courses that customers can choose?

c The same restaurant offers a standard three-course menu and boasts that it allows '1001 different combinations'.
What can you conclude about the number of starters, main courses and sweets that customers can choose?

6 Four houses are arranged so that there is a direct path joining each pair of houses.
How many paths are there altogether?

7 **a** How many two-digit integers have both digits odd?

 b How many two-digit integers have both digits even?

 c How many two-digit integers have one odd digit and one even digit?

8 In this *word sum*, I, M, O, N, T and P stand for different non-zero digits. (For this problem, it may help to tackle T3 *Word sums A* first.)

$$\begin{array}{r} I\,'\;M \\ +\;O\;\;N \\ \hline T\;O\;\;P \end{array}$$

 a Which digits are uniquely determined? Explain.

 b What is the smallest possible value for M?

 c **i** Suppose M = 2 or 3.
 How many possible values are there for N?
 How many possible solutions are there for the complete sum?

 ii Suppose M = 4.
 How many possible values are there for N?
 How many possible solutions are there for the complete sum?

 iii Suppose M = 5.
 How many possible values are there for N?
 How many possible solutions are there for the complete sum?

 iv Suppose M = 6.
 How many possible values are there for N?
 How many possible solutions are there for the complete sum?

 v Suppose M = 7.
 How many possible values are there for N?
 How many possible solutions are there for the complete sum?

 vi Suppose M = 8.
 How many possible values are there for N?
 How many possible solutions are there for the complete sum?

T14　Word problems *A*　　　NC

Tackling *word problems* is the simplest and the most basic way you learn to *use* elementary mathematics. Arithmetic often gets stuck in a world of numbers and numerals. It takes practice and effort to make elementary arithmetic part of the way you think about the *real* world. Word problems are not 'real', but they help to develop the skills needed to link the world of mathematics to the 'real' world.

Problem 0

0 A father and son live in the same house and walk to work at the same factory.

a Suppose the father covers the distance in 40 minutes and the son in 30 minutes.
If the son leaves home five minutes after his father, after how long does he overtake his father?

b Suppose the father covers the distance in 48 minutes and the son in 42 minutes.
If the son leaves home two minutes after his father, after how long does he overtake his father?

Each problem is given in *words,* so you must

◎　read it carefully (from the beginning *to the end*)

◎　sort out what you have to do

◎　extract the information from the problem as stated

◎　do the necessary calculation to get the required answer.

1 Class 8*X* are lined up for a photo. Di is 9th from the left-hand end and 18th from the right-hand end.
How many children are there in the class?

2 A train leaves Station *A* at 9:40 am and arrives at Station *B* five miles away at 9:48 am.
What is the average speed of the train on this section of its journey?

3 The average age of five students is 15 years 0 months. The first student is 14 years 0 months; the second student is 16 years 0 months; the third student is 17 years 3 months; the fourth student is 13 year 9 months. How old is the fifth student?

4 You are told that 56 % of the pupils in a class are girls.
What is the smallest number of pupils the class could contain?

5 Chickens and rabbits are running around outside in the farmyard.
Together they have 35 heads and 94 feet.
How many rabbits are there?

6 Fence posts are erected 5 m apart (with a post at each corner) to
support fencing round a rectangular field.
If the field measures 100 m by 60 m, how many posts are needed?

7 My two piggy banks contain 140 p between them. If 15 p were
shifted from one piggy bank to the other, there would be equal
amounts in each. How much is there in each piggy bank?

8 One hundred and forty thick notebooks and one hundred
thin notebooks were made using 7340 sheets of paper altogether.
Each thick notebook used one more sheet of paper than each thin
notebook.
How many sheets of paper were used to make each thick
notebook?
How many sheets of paper were used for each thin notebook?

9 A boy spent $\frac{3}{8}$ of his allowance and put $\frac{1}{2}$ of the remainder in
the bank. He then had £ 15 left.
How much money did he have to start with?

10 35 % of pupils in a school are boys. 20 % of the girls are 14 years old
or more. There are 260 girls below age 14.
How many boys are there in the school?

11 100 loaves of bread are shared by 100 monks. Some monks are old
and some are young novices. Each old monk gets 3 loaves, but
3 young novices have to share a loaf.
How many old monks are there?
How many novices?

T15 Drawing conclusions *B*: Asking why?

If a bunch of roses arrives on your doorstep, it is probably no accident! It is reasonable to assume that someone sent them, and that they are trying to tell you something.

When something unexpected happens in mathematics, there is usually a reason, and you should want to know *why* it happens. It may take some time before you can understand completely, but the important things are

◎ to carry out instructions *accurately* so that you give yourself a chance of noticing anything unexpected

◎ to keep alert and keep thinking – so that you notice when something is indeed unexpected.

In the problems in this section, make sure you have a sharp pencil and a ruler, and that you measure accurately.

Problem 0

---

0 Draw a line segment *AB* of length 9 cm.
Use a protractor centred at *A* and lined up along *AB* to mark a point *X* with ∠*BAX* = 90°. Draw the *ray AX*.

a Mark the point *D* on *AX* with *AD* = 10 cm. Measure *BD*.

b Mark the point *C* on *AX* with *AC* = 12 cm. Measure *BC*.

Which gives rise to the more interesting measurement: part **a** or part **b**?

---

1 a Draw a line segment *AB* of length exactly 18 cm.
Use a protractor centred at *A* and lined up along *AB* to mark a point *X* with ∠*BAX* = 90°. Draw the ray *AX*. Mark the point *C* on *AX* with *AC* = 24 cm. Measure *BC*.

b What is the connection between the outcome of part **a** and problem **0b**? Explain your answer.

2 a Draw a line segment *AB* of length exactly 10 cm.
Use a protractor centred at *A* and lined up along *AB* to mark a point *X* with ∠*BAX* = 90°. Draw the ray *AX*. Mark the point *C* on *AX* with *AC* = 24 cm. Measure *BC*.

b Can you see a possible connection between the outcome of part **a** and problems **0b, 1a**?

3   Draw a line segment *MA* exactly 17.3 cm long.
    Use a protractor centred at *M* and lined up along *MA* to mark
    a point *X* with $\angle AMX = 90°$. Draw the line *MX* and mark the
    points *B*, *C* on *MX* (extended if necessary) with *MB* = *MC* = 10 cm,
    BC = 20 cm.

    a   Measure *AB* and *AC*.

    b   Measure $\angle ABC$, $\angle BCA$, $\angle CAB$.

    c   What seems to be (approximately) true of $\triangle ABC$?

4   Draw a line segment *BD* exactly 28.3 cm long.
    Mark the point *X* on *BD* such that *BX* = 20 cm, *DX* = 8.3 cm.
    Mark the point *Y* on *BD* such that *BY* = 8.3 cm, *DY* = 20 cm.
    Draw the circle with centre *B* and passing through *X*; draw the
    circle with centre *D* and passing through *Y*. Let these two circles
    meet at *A* and *C*.

    a   What can you say *without measuring* about the lengths of
        AB, *BC*, *CD*, *DA*? Explain your answer.

    b   Measure $\angle ABC$, $\angle ADB$.
        What does this suggest about $\angle DAB$?

    c   What seems to be (approximately) true about the quadrilateral *ABCD*?

5   Draw a line segment *AD* of length 20 cm.
    Mark the point *O* on *AD* such that *AO* = *OD* = 10 cm.
    Draw the circle, $\mathcal{C}$, with centre *O* and passing through *A* (and *D*);
    draw the circle with centre *A* and passing through *O*.
    Let these two circles meet at *B* and *F*.
    Draw the circle with centre *D* and passing through *O*; let it meet
    the first circle, $\mathcal{C}$, at *C* and *E* (with *C* between *B* and *D*).

    a   Join *AB*, *BC*, *CD*, *DE*, *EF*, *FA*.

    b   What can you say (without measuring) about the lengths of *AB*,
        AF, *DC*, *DE*?

    c   Measure *BC*, *EF*. Is this approximate? Or is there some reason
        that guarantees these lengths must be equal to *AO*?

    d   What can you say about $\angle OAB$, $\angle OBA$, $\angle OAF$, $\angle OFA$ (without
        measuring)?
        What can you say about $\angle ODC$, $\angle OCD$, $\angle ODE$, $\angle OED$ (without
        measuring)?

    e   Measure $\angle OBC$, $\angle OCB$, $\angle OEF$, $\angle OFE$.

    f   What appears to be true about the hexagon *ABCDEF*?

    Explain how you could have *proved* this on the basis of the
    construction (without measuring).

6 Draw a line segment *AE* of length 28.3 cm.

Draw the circle with centre *A* and passing through *E*, and the circle with centre *E* and passing through *A*. Let these two circles meet at *X* and *Y*.

Draw the line *XY* and let this cut *AE* at *O* (the *i**oi** of *AE*).

Draw the circle, *C*, with centre *O* and passing through *A* and let this meet *XY* at *C* and *G*.

a **i** Measure *AC*, *CE*, *EG*, *GA*.

    ii Measure ∠*ACE*, ∠*CEG*, ∠*EGA*, ∠*GAC*.

    iii What seems to be true about the quadrilateral *ACEG*?

    iv Explain how you could have *proved* your guess in part **iii** by using the fact that △*OAC* and △*OEC* are i*o**e*e* (assuming that *XY* is the perpendicular bisector of *AE*).

b Mark the mid-point *S* of *AC*, the mid-point *T* of *CE*, the mid-point *U* of *EG*, and the mid-point *V* of *GA*.

Let the circle, *C* (with centre *O*), meet *TV* at *D* and *H* (with *D* between *C* and *E*), and let *C* meet *SU* at *B* and *F* (with *B* between *A* and *C*).

    i Measure *AB*, *BC*, *CD*, *DE*, *EF*, *FG*, *GH*, *HA*.

    Measure ∠*ABC*, ∠*BCD*, ∠*CDE*, ∠*DEF*, ∠*EFG*, ∠*FGH*, ∠*GHA*, ∠*HAB*.

    ii What seems to be true about the octagon *ABCDEFGH*?

    iii Explain how you could have *proved* this without measuring.

T16 Simplifying fractions *A*   NC

The most basic technique when working with fractions is to notice when a messy looking fraction is in fact something simple in disguise. You need to move easily and accurately between different ways of writing the same fraction. In other words, you need to be able to *simplify*.

Problem 0

0 a Simplify $\dfrac{1 + 2 + 3 + 4 + 5}{12345}$.

b Simplify $\dfrac{4 + 8}{4 \times 8}$.

Mathematics derives its power from the fact that simple objects can be written in more than one way (think about $2 + 2$ and 4, or $10^2 - 1^2$ and $(10 - 1)(10 + 1)$). In the middle of any calculation, numbers and expressions arise that are messy; to avoid errors it is always wise to *simplify*.

Fractions can be simplified whenever the numerator and denominator have a common factor. One way to simplify is to evaluate the numerator and denominator, and then look to cancel common factors. But you can often see common factors without evaluating, for example,

$$\frac{4 + 8}{4 \times 8} = \frac{4(1 + 2)}{4 \times 8} = \frac{1 + 2}{8} = \frac{\Box}{8}$$

1 Simplify these fractions.

a $\dfrac{1 + 2}{12} =$

b $\dfrac{1 + 5}{15} =$

c $\dfrac{3 + 6}{36} =$

d $\dfrac{4 + 2}{42} =$

e $\dfrac{2 + 8}{28} =$

f $\dfrac{4 + 8}{48} =$

g $\dfrac{6 + 6}{66} =$

h $\dfrac{2 + 7}{27} =$

i $\dfrac{8 + 4}{84} =$

j $\dfrac{4 + 5}{45} =$

k $\dfrac{2 + 1}{21} =$

l $\dfrac{7 + 5}{75} =$

m $\dfrac{6 + 3}{63} =$

n $\dfrac{7 + 2}{72} =$

o $\dfrac{8 + 1}{81} =$

2 Simplify these fractions.

a $\dfrac{1+1+1}{111} =$ **e** $\dfrac{1+3+5}{135} =$

b $\dfrac{1+2+3}{123} =$ **f** $\dfrac{2+4+6}{246} =$

c $\dfrac{1+4+5}{145} =$ **g** $\dfrac{4+6+8}{468} =$

d $\dfrac{2+3+4}{234} =$ **h** $\dfrac{4+4+8}{448} =$

3 Simplify these fractions.

a $\dfrac{4+6}{4\times6} =$ **g** $\dfrac{4+5+6}{4\times5\times6} =$

b $\dfrac{2+8}{2\times8} =$ **h** $\dfrac{1+2+3}{1\times2\times3} =$

c $\dfrac{3+6}{3\times6} =$ **i** $\dfrac{3+5+7}{3\times5\times7} =$

d $\dfrac{6+8}{6\times8} =$ **j** $\dfrac{5+7+9}{5\times7\times9} =$

e $\dfrac{2+3+4}{2\times3\times4} =$ **k** $\dfrac{1+5+9}{1\times5\times9} =$

f $\dfrac{2+4+6}{2\times4\times6} =$ **l** $\dfrac{1+3+5}{1\times3\times5} =$

4 Simplify these fractions.

a $\dfrac{12}{34} =$ **e** $\dfrac{456}{78} =$

b $\dfrac{123}{45} =$ **f** $\dfrac{87}{6543} =$

c $\dfrac{12}{3456} =$ **g** $\dfrac{345}{67\,890} =$

d $\dfrac{123}{456} =$ **h** $\dfrac{234}{567} =$

39

T17 Calculating angles *A*

If you know *some* of the angles in a geometrical figure, you can often work out *other* angles exactly – using these *four basic facts*.

◎ Angles on a straight line add to ___°.

◎ Vertically opposite angles are ___.

◎ The two base angles of any isosceles triangle are ___.

◎ The three angles in any triangle add to ___°.

Problem 0

0 In the quadrilateral *ABCD* the sizes of three angles are given.

  a Work out the size of the angles marked *w* and *x*.
     Justify your answers.

  b What can you prove about △*ABC*?

  c Can you calculate the sizes of the angles marked *y* and *z*?

Use the given information to work out the unknown marked angles.

1

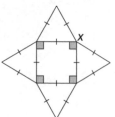

3

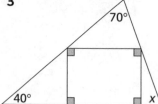

5

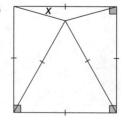

2

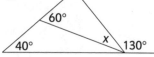

4

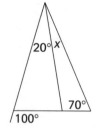

6

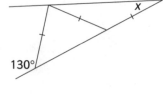

7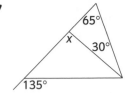

9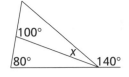

11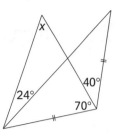

8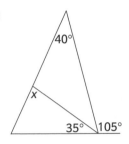

10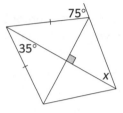

12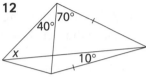

13 a In the quadrilateral *ABCD* the sizes of three angles are given.

    i Work out the size of $y + z$.

    ii Can you work out the sizes '*y*' and '*z*'?

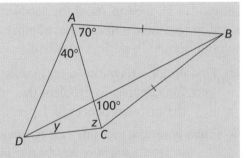

  b i Draw the figure in part **a** (with $\angle BAC = 70°$) as accurately as you can, choosing the scale of your diagram by making $AB = 10\,\text{cm}$.

    ii Since $\angle BAC = \underline{}$ and $\angle ABC = \underline{}$ are given, the position of the point *C* is fixed.

    Since $\angle BAD = \underline{}$ and $\angle ABD = \underline{}$ are given, the position of the point *D* is fixed.

    ∴ $\angle ACD$ and $\angle BDC$ are determined (even though they cannot be calculated using the methods you know).

    iii Measure $\angle ACD$ and $\angle BDC$ in your diagram to find their approximate sizes.

T18 Equations   NC

Problem 0

> **0 a** I bought seven pencils, paid with a £2 coin and received 18p change. How much did each pencil cost?
>
> **b** A box of 42 drawing pins weighs 84 g. The contents weigh 28 g more than the box. What is the weight of a single drawing pin?

Easy problems of this kind can be solved mentally using *inverse arithmetic*, but harder problems are best solved using *letters* to stand for *unknown numbers*. This has the great advantage that it makes all such problems equally easy. The goal of this section is for you to learn to write out solutions to problems of this kind *using a standard layout*.

Letters can be used to stand for *numbers*; letters should *not* be used to stand for *quantities* – that is, for numbers with attached units. So every solution should begin in a standard way:

◎ First decide which (unknown) *number* you wish to represent by a *letter*, for example, in problem **0a** it makes sense to take
'the price (in pence) of 1 pencil'.

◎ Then write the first line: '*Let the price of each pencil be x pence*',
or '*Let the weight of one drawing pin be d grams*'.

Solution 0a: Let each pencil cost x pence.

$\therefore 200 = 7x + 18$ (£2 is cost of 7 pencils + 18p change)

$\therefore 7x = 182$

$\therefore x = \underline{\quad}$, so each pencil costs $\underline{\quad}$ pence.

Problem **0b** is more complicated. Here it makes sense to give 'letter-names' to *two* numbers, and then to *eliminate* one of the letters.

Solution 0b: Let the box weigh b grams

and let each drawing pin weigh d grams.

(∗) $b + 42d = \underline{\quad}$ (Box plus drawing pins together weigh $\underline{\quad}$ grams)

and $42d = b + 28$ (contents weigh $\underline{\quad}$ grams more than the box)

$\therefore b = 42d - \underline{\quad}$

$\therefore (42d - \underline{\quad}) + 42d = 84$ (substitute '$b = 42d - \underline{\quad}$' in (∗))

$\therefore 84d = \underline{\quad}$, so $d = \underline{\quad}$ and a drawing pin weighs $\underline{\quad}$ grams.

In each of the following problems, copy the given layout and fill in the gaps to find the solution.

1 (*Alpha* T22) My Christmas present cost £1.20 plus one-third of its price. What did it cost?

    Let the price of my Christmas present be c pence.

$\therefore c = \underline{\quad} + \frac{1}{3}c$ $\therefore \frac{2}{3}c = \underline{\quad}$, so my present cost £$\underline{\quad}$

2 (*Alpha* C21) When a tank is two-thirds full it contains 120 litres.
How much does it contain when it is three-quarters full?

Let the tank contain t litres when full.

$\therefore \frac{2}{3} t =$ ___ $\therefore \frac{1}{3} t =$ ___ $\therefore t =$ ___

$\therefore \frac{3}{4} t =$ ___, so a three-quarters full tank contains ___ litres.

3 (*Alpha* T26) A milk bottle weighs 410 g when one-quarter full, and
460 g when one-third full. What does the bottle weigh
a when full? b when half-full?

Let the weight of the bottle be b grams and the weight of the
liquid be x grams when the bottle is full.

$\therefore b + \frac{1}{4} x =$ ___ and $b + \frac{1}{3} x =$ ___

$\therefore \frac{1}{3} x - \frac{1}{4} x =$ ___, so $x =$ ___, $b =$ ___.

4 (*Alpha* T22)

a Three friends earned £200 cutting lawns. They reckoned that
John and Mark did three times as much work between them as
Ben, and that Mark did twice as much as John. How much of the
money should go to John?

Let the amounts each deserves be £b (Ben), £j (John) and £m (Mark).

$\therefore m = 2j$ (Mark did twice as much work as John)

and $m + j = 3b$ (John and Mark together did three times as
                  much work as Ben)

$\therefore$ ___ + ___ = 3b, so $j =$ ___.

$\therefore$ John should receive £ ___.

b On another occasion they earned £180 by cutting lawns. This
time John did half as much as Ben and Mark combined, and Ben did
twice as much as Mark. How much of the money should go to Ben?

5 (*Alpha* T14) I bought a cat and a dog, and then sold them for £60
each. I made a 20% profit on the sale of the dog and a 20% loss on
the sale of the cat. How much money did I make or lose?

Let the price I paid for the dog be £d and the price I paid for
the cat be £c.

$\therefore \frac{120}{100} d =$ ___ and $\frac{80}{100} c =$ ___. $\therefore d =$ ___ and $c =$ ___

$\therefore$ Net (overall) gain = $2 \times 60 - (d + c) =$ ___, so I actually ___ £ ___.

6 (*Alpha* C12) The total of the ages of a father, his daughter and his
two sons is 96 years. The daughter's age is half the father's age
and twice the age of each of her two brothers. How old is the father?

Let the age of each of the two sons be s years.

$\therefore$ Daughter's age = ___ (daughter's age is ___ age of each brother)

and father's age = ___ (daughter's age is ___ the father's age)

$\therefore 96 =$ sum of all four ages = ___ + ___ + 2s

$\therefore s =$ ___, so the father's age is ___.

7 (*Alpha* C21) It takes me 21 minutes to walk to work at 6 km per hour. How long would it take me if I could manage 7 km per hour?

    Let the distance to work be w km.

    21 minutes is $\frac{21}{60}$ of an hour; $\therefore w = \frac{21}{60} \times \underline{\quad}$.

    If I could walk at 7 km per hour, then I could manage 1 km in $\underline{\quad}$ hour,

    so w km would take me $w \times \underline{\quad} = \left(\frac{21}{60} \times 6\right) \times \underline{\quad}$ hours, or $\underline{\quad}$ minutes.

8 (*Alpha* C21) Two numbers are in the ratio 7 : 3. If their difference is 24, what are the two numbers?

    Let the two numbers be n and m, with $n : m = 7 : 3$.

    $\therefore \underline{\quad} n = \underline{\quad} m$ $\therefore 21n = \underline{\quad} m$

    Also $n - m = \underline{\quad}$ (the difference between the two numbers is $\underline{\quad}$)

    $\therefore 21(n - m) = 21n - 21m = \underline{\quad} m$

    $\therefore 21 \times 24 = 21(n - m) = \underline{\quad} m$

    $\therefore m = \underline{\quad}$ and $n = \underline{\quad}$.

9 Two rods with lengths 55 cm and 42 cm are shortened by the same amount until one rod is exactly twice as long as the other. How long are they then? ("*Let the amount removed from each rod be x cm.*")

10 A 'cheap day return' is one-quarter of the standard fare, and saves me £6.18. What is the standard fare? ("*Let the standard fare be x pence.*")

11 My mother is twenty-six years older than I am. Next year she will be three times as old as me. How old am I (in years)? ("*Let my mother's age now be x years.*")

12 A school shop buys some oranges at 10 p each. One dozen are rotten, but by selling the rest at 20 p, they manage to make £4.80 profit. How many oranges did they buy?

13 In 3 years from now Steve will be 3 times as old as he was 3 years ago. How old is he?

14 I bought 20 calculators for £108; some cost £4.50 and the rest cost £7.50. How many of the cheaper kind did I buy?

15 A large jar of marmalade weighs 3.2 kg when half full and 2.3 kg when one-quarter full. What is the weight of the jar when full?

16 a Find k if '$3k$ minutes past four' is the same as '$2k$ minutes to five'.

    b Find k if '$5k$ minutes past four' is the same as '$7k$ minutes to five'.

    c Find k if '$3k - 1$ minutes past four' is the same as '$2k + 1$ minutes to five'.

17 A man leaves P at 1 pm and walks to Q at 6 km per hour. A woman leaves Q at 3 pm and cycles to P at 16 km per hour.

    i They cross at t pm. Write how many kilometres each has travelled in terms of t.

    ii If the distance from P to Q is 45 km, form an equation and find the value of t.

18 100 loaves of bread are shared by 100 monks. Some monks are old and some are young novices. Each old monk gets 3 loaves, but the young novices have to share one loaf between 3. How many old monks are there and how many novices?

Problem 0

0 a i Factorise 6 as a product of powers of prime numbers:

$6 = \_\_^{\square} \times \_\_^{\square}$

ii Use this prime factorisation of 6 to write down all the factors of 6:

$6 = \_\_^{\square} \times \_\_^{\square}$;

∴ factors are $\_\_^{0} \times \_\_^{0} = 1$, and $\_\_^{0} \times \_\_^{1} = \_\_$

$\_\_^{1} \times \_\_^{0} = \_\_$, and $\_\_^{1} \times \_\_^{1} = \_\_$

b i Factorise 12 as a product of powers of prime numbers:

$12 = \_\_^{\square} \times \_\_^{\square}$

ii Use this prime factorisation of 12 to write down all the factors of 12:

$12 = \_\_^{\square} \times \_\_^{\square}$;

∴ factors are $\_\_^{0} \times \_\_^{0} = 1$, and $\_\_^{0} \times \_\_^{1} = \_\_$

$\_\_^{1} \times \_\_^{0} = \_\_$, and $\_\_^{1} \times \_\_^{1} = \_\_$

$\_\_^{2} \times \_\_^{0} = \_\_$, and $\_\_^{2} \times \_\_^{1} = \_\_$

c i Factorise 36 as a product of powers of prime numbers:

$36 = \_\_^{\square} \times \_\_^{\square}$

ii Use this prime factorisation of 36 to write down all the factors of 36.

Each integer ≥2 can be *factorised* as a product of powers of prime numbers.

$6 = 2 \times 3 \qquad 12 = 2 \times 2 \times 3 = 2^2 \times 3$

As long as you remember to *collect up* repeated prime factors, all the factors of a given integer can be read off from the prime factorisation.

For example, the factors of $6 = 2 \times 3 = 2^1 \times 3^1$

are $\qquad 2^0 \times 3^0 = 1$, and $2^0 \times 3^1 = \_\_$

$2^1 \times 3^0 = \_\_$, and $2^1 \times 3^1 = \_\_$

To sum up, because $6 = 2^1 \times 3^1$, each factor of 6 is the product of:

a *power* of 2 (2^0 or 2^1) and a *power* of 3 (3^0 or 3^1).

So 6 has exactly 2×2 factors – just as the mouse in Section T13 had exactly 3×2 routes to the cheese.

Similarly $12 = 2^2 \times 3 = 2^2 \times 3^1$, so the factors of 12 are

are $\qquad 2^0 \times 3^0 = 1$, and $2^0 \times 3^1 = \_\_$

$2^1 \times 3^0 = \_\_$, and $2^1 \times 3^1 = \_\_$

$2^2 \times 3^0 = \_\_$, and $2^2 \times 3^1 = \_\_$

To sum up, because $12 = 2^2 \times 3^1$, each factor of 12 is the product of:
  a *power of 2* (2^0, or 2^1, or 2^2) and *a power of 3* (3^0 or 3^1).

So 12 has exactly 3×2 factors. This idea is developed further in **E8**.

Factorise each of the following integers N as a product of powers of *different* prime numbers. Use this to write straightaway the *number of* factors N has; then make a *list* (in a systematic order) of all possible factors of the given integer.

1 $15 = 3^1 \times$ ___
  $\therefore$ factors are $3^0 \times$ ___, $3^0 \times$ ___; $3^1 \times$ ___, and $3^1 \times$ ___

2 $22 = 2^1 \times$ ___
  $\therefore$ factors are $2^0 \times$ ___, $2^0 \times$ ___; $2^1 \times$ ___, and $2^1 \times$ ___

3 $35 =$ ___
  $\therefore$ factors are ___ , ___ ; ___ , ___

4 $51 =$	**10** $45 =$	**16** $24 =$
5 $65 =$	**11** $63 =$	**17** $54 =$
6 $91 =$	**12** $98 =$	**18** $135 =$
7 $143 =$	**13** $75 =$	**19** $189 =$
8 $20 =$	**14** $242 =$	**20** $250 =$
9 $28 =$	**15** $245 =$	

21 **a** Complete $64 =$ ___^{2} and $64 =$ ___^{3}.

  b What is the next integer that is both a square and a cube?

T20   Types of triangle

T A S T E R

A triangle is *more* than just a shape – it is a *labelled* shape.
Consider the labelled triangle *ABC*.
The side *BC opposite* the vertex **A** has length *a*.
Similarly the side *CA opposite* vertex **B** has length *b*.
And the side *AB opposite* vertex **C** has length *c*.

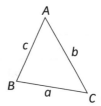

Triangles are described in terms of their sides or in terms of their angles.

Side types Triangle *ABC*

◎   is **equilateral** if all three sides are equal: $AB = BC = CA$

◎   is **isosceles** (*with base BC and apex A*) if $AB = AC$.

A triangle in which all three sides have different lengths is not nearly as interesting – and is said to be **scalene**.

Angle types Triangle *ABC*

◎   is **right-angled** if *one* of the three angles is equal to 90°

◎   is **acute-angled** if *all three* angles are acute (that is, less than 90°)

◎   is **obtuse-angled** if *one* angle is obtuse (that is, greater than 90°).

Problem 0

> **0** Each row in the table on the next page describes a single triangle *ABC*. *Your job is to fill in the blanks.*
> If there is no unique shortest or longest side, leave that entry blank. (If you are unsure what answer to write, use a ruler and protractor to construct an *accurate* copy of the triangle and measure the relevant angle or side in your diagram).

47

	Angle A	Angle B	Angle C	Angle type	Side type	Longest side	Shortest side	Largest angle	Smallest angle
Triangle	61°	23°	96°	obtuse	scalene	c	b	C	B
1	117°	31°							
2	73°	81°							
3	44°	46°							
4	60°		60°						
5	60°			right angle			c		
6	37°	51°							
7	33°	74°							
8	90°				isosceles				
9	32°				isosceles		a		
10	32°				isosceles	b			

1 For each of the following questions state whether it is possible to draw such a triangle. If it is not possible, explain why not.
Can a triangle be:

    a isosceles and acute-angled?   **f** isosceles and obtuse-angled?

    b isosceles and right-angled?   **g** equilateral and obtuse-angled?

    c equilateral and right-angled?   **h** scalene and right-angled?

    d scalene and acute-angled?   **i** scalene and obtuse-angled?

    e equilateral and acute-angled?

2 Look back at your completed table in problem **0**.
(Each of the triangles **1**, **3**, **4** and **7** have two angles that are equal, or almost equal, in size, so, if you measured rather than calculated, your entries may have been affected by measurement errors).

    a In triangle **2**

       i Which is the smallest angle: *A*, or *B*, or *C*?

      ii Which is the shortest side: *a*, or *b*, or *c*?

    b In triangle **5**

       i Which is the smallest angle: *A*, or *B*, or *C*?

      ii Which is the shortest side: *a*, or *b*, or *c*?

    c In triangle **6**

       i Which is the smallest angle: *A*, or *B*, or *C*?

      ii Which is the shortest side: *a*, or *b*, or *c*?

d In triangle **9**

   i Which is the smallest angle: *A*, or *B*, or *C*?

   ii Which is the shortest side: *a*, or *b*, or *c*?

3 Use the examples in your table to answer these questions.

  a How do you think the smallest angle and the shortest side in a triangle are related?

  b How do you think the largest angle and the longest side are related?

Until you can *prove* what you noticed in problem **3**, the result remains an experimental observation.

A geometrical proof depends on the *Exterior Angle Theorem* ('each exterior angle of a triangle is equal to the sum of the two interior opposite angles' – see C11 *Calculating angles B*).

A proof using trigonometry uses the *sine rule,* which you should meet in a year or two's time.

T21 Highest common factors and least common multiples *A* NC

The *highest common factor* (or *hcf*) of 12 and 18 is 6:   hcf(12, 18) = 6.
The *least common multiple* (*lcm*) of 12 and 18 is 36:   lcm(18, 12) = 36.

Problem 0

0 a Find the *hcf* and *lcm* of 66 and 99.
  hcf(66, 99) = ___   lcm(66, 99) = ___

b Find the *hcf* and *lcm* of 135 and 189.
  hcf(135, 189) = ___   lcm(135, 189) = ___

To find the *hcf* and *lcm* of two integers, find the *hcf* first. For example,
  to find *hcf*(135, 189), look for common factors.
    2 is not an option (since 135 is o∗∗);
    so try 3:
      135 = 3 × 45 = 3 × 3 × 15 = 3 × 3 × 3 × 5 = <u>27</u> × 5
      189 = 3 × 63 = 3 × 3 × 21 = 3 × 3 × 3 × 7 = <u>27</u> × 7
    ∴ *hcf*(135, 189) = 27
      135 = 5 × 27, 189 = 27 × 7
    ∴ *lcm*(135, 189) = 5 × 189 *(leave your answer in factorised form)*.

1 36 and 84:   hcf(36, 84)   =   lcm(36, 84)   =
2 60 and 156:   hcf(60, 156)   =   lcm(60, 156)   =
3 45 and 162:   hcf(45, 162)   =   lcm(45, 162)   =
4 99 and 264:   hcf(99, 264)   =   lcm(99, 264)   =
5 105 and 147: hcf(105, 147) =   lcm(105, 147) =
6 345 and 405: hcf(345, 405) =   lcm(345, 405) =
7 252 and 1728: hcf(252, 1728) =   lcm(252, 1728) =
8 648 and 672: hcf(648, 672) =   lcm(648, 672) =
9 648 and 675: hcf(648, 675) =   lcm(648, 675) =
10 665 and 1190: hcf(665, 1190) =   lcm(665, 1190) =
11 253 and 460: hcf(253, 460) =   lcm(253, 460) =

12 a A 54 × 78 rectangle is to be cut into equal-sized squares, which are to be as large as possible. How large will each of these squares be?

How many squares are there altogether?

b A company markets square carpet tiles in two sizes: 45 mm × 45 mm, and 162 mm × 162 mm. They use a *single* size of cardboard box, with a square cross-section, to pack *both* types of tiles.

What is the smallest possible square cross-section for such a cardboard box?

How many of each tile would there be in a single layer in such a box?

13 HCFs are important when simplifying fractions. Simplify (that is, cancel down) each of these fractions as much as possible.

a $\dfrac{5}{10}$ =

b $\dfrac{6}{12}$ =

c $\dfrac{5}{20}$ =

d $\dfrac{12}{15}$ =

e $\dfrac{9}{12}$ =

f $\dfrac{15}{20}$ =

g $\dfrac{24}{16}$ =

h $\dfrac{20}{30}$ =

i $\dfrac{48}{60}$ =

j $\dfrac{156}{60}$ =

k $\dfrac{45}{162}$ =

l $\dfrac{99}{264}$ =

m $\dfrac{147}{105}$ =

n $\dfrac{143}{88}$ =

o $\dfrac{345}{405}$ =

p $\dfrac{252}{1728}$ =

q $\dfrac{648}{672}$ =

r $\dfrac{665}{1190}$ =

s $\dfrac{253}{460}$ =

14 LCMs are important when adding fractions. Add these fractions and simplify your answer as much as possible.

a $\dfrac{1}{15} + \dfrac{1}{20}$ =

b $\dfrac{1}{16} + \dfrac{1}{24}$ =

c $\dfrac{1}{45} + \dfrac{3}{162}$ =

d $\dfrac{1}{99} + \dfrac{1}{264}$ =

e $\dfrac{1}{105} + \dfrac{1}{147}$ =

f $\dfrac{3}{665} + \dfrac{2}{1190}$ =

T22 Adding and subtracting fractions *A*   NC

The key to the arithmetic of fractions lies in making an appropriate choice of *unit*.

Problem 0

0 a $\frac{1}{3} + \frac{1}{6} =$ **b** $\frac{1}{10} - \frac{1}{15} =$

To combine $\frac{1}{3}$ and $\frac{1}{6}$, both fractions must be expressed using a *common unit*. Fortunately $\frac{1}{3} = 2 \times \frac{1}{6}$, so you can use $\frac{1}{6}$ as a common unit.

$$\therefore \frac{1}{3} + \frac{1}{6} = 2 \times \frac{1}{6} + 1 \times \frac{1}{6} = \underline{\quad} \times \frac{1}{6} =$$

What common unit can be used to express both $\frac{1}{10}$ and $\frac{1}{15}$?

$\frac{1}{10}$ is the same as $3 \times \frac{1}{\square}$, and $\frac{1}{15}$ is the same as $2 \times \frac{1}{\square}$.

$$\therefore \frac{1}{10} - \frac{1}{15} = 3 \times \frac{1}{\square} - 2 \times \frac{1}{\square} = \underline{\quad} \times \frac{1}{\square} =$$

Work out each sum by expressing the two fractions using a common unit.

1 $\frac{1}{2} - \frac{1}{3} \quad = \underline{\quad} \times \frac{1}{\square} - \underline{\quad} \times \frac{1}{\square} = \underline{\quad} \times \frac{1}{\square} =$

2 a $\frac{1}{2} + \frac{1}{6} \quad = \underline{\quad} \times \frac{1}{\square} + \underline{\quad} \times \frac{1}{\square} = \underline{\quad} \times \frac{1}{\square} =$

   b $\frac{1}{4} + \frac{1}{12} =$

   c $\frac{1}{3} + \frac{1}{6} =$

   d $\frac{1}{4} - \frac{1}{6} =$

3 a $\frac{1}{3} - \frac{1}{4} \quad = \underline{\quad} \times \frac{1}{\square} - \underline{\quad} \times \frac{1}{\square} = \underline{\quad} \times \frac{1}{\square} =$

   b $\frac{1}{4} - \frac{1}{5} =$

   c $\frac{1}{5} - \frac{1}{6} =$

   d $\frac{1}{6} - \frac{1}{7} =$

4 a $\dfrac{2}{1} - \dfrac{2}{2} =$

b $\dfrac{2}{2} - \dfrac{2}{3} =$

c $\dfrac{2}{3} - \dfrac{2}{4} =$

d $\dfrac{2}{4} - \dfrac{2}{5} =$

e $\dfrac{2}{5} - \dfrac{2}{6} =$

5 a $\dfrac{1}{3} - \dfrac{1}{6} =$

b $\dfrac{1}{6} - \dfrac{1}{10} =$

c $\dfrac{1}{10} - \dfrac{1}{15} =$

d $\dfrac{1}{15} - \dfrac{1}{21} =$

e $\dfrac{1}{21} - \dfrac{1}{28} =$

f $\dfrac{1}{28} - \dfrac{1}{36} =$

g $\dfrac{1}{36} - \dfrac{1}{45} =$

h $\dfrac{1}{45} - \dfrac{1}{55} =$

i $\dfrac{1}{55} - \dfrac{1}{66} =$

6 a $\dfrac{1}{1} \times \dfrac{1}{2} + \dfrac{1}{2} \times \dfrac{1}{3} =$

b $\dfrac{1}{2} \times \dfrac{1}{3} + \dfrac{1}{3} \times \dfrac{1}{4} =$

c $\dfrac{1}{3} \times \dfrac{1}{4} + \dfrac{1}{4} \times \dfrac{1}{5} =$

d $\dfrac{1}{4} \times \dfrac{1}{5} + \dfrac{1}{5} \times \dfrac{1}{6} =$

7 Work out $\dfrac{1}{10} + \dfrac{1}{20} + \dfrac{1}{30} + \dfrac{1}{50} + \dfrac{1}{60} + \dfrac{1}{200}$
and simplify the answer.

8 a $\dfrac{1}{1} \times \dfrac{1}{2} + \dfrac{1}{2} \times \dfrac{1}{3} =$

b $\dfrac{1}{1} \times \dfrac{1}{2} + \dfrac{1}{2} \times \dfrac{1}{3} + \dfrac{1}{3} \times \dfrac{1}{4} =$

c $\dfrac{1}{1} \times \dfrac{1}{2} + \dfrac{1}{2} \times \dfrac{1}{3} + \dfrac{1}{3} \times \dfrac{1}{4} + \dfrac{1}{4} \times \dfrac{1}{5} =$

d $\dfrac{1}{1} \times \dfrac{1}{2} + \dfrac{1}{2} \times \dfrac{1}{3} + \dfrac{1}{3} \times \dfrac{1}{4} + \dfrac{1}{4} \times \dfrac{1}{5} + \dfrac{1}{5} \times \dfrac{1}{6} =$

TASTER

The place value system for writing *integers* is based on 10s, 100s, 1000s, and so on. The place value system for writing *decimals* is based on 10^{ths}, 100^{ths}, 1000^{ths}, and so on. This makes some multiplications especially important, for example

$$10 \times \frac{1}{10} = \frac{10}{10} = \underline{\quad}$$

$$\therefore 20 \times \frac{1}{10} = 2 \times \left(10 \times \frac{1}{10}\right) = \underline{\quad}$$

$$\therefore 100 \times \frac{1}{10} = 10 \times \left(\underline{\quad}\right) = \underline{\quad}$$

You can write these using decimals

$$10 \times 0.1 = \underline{\quad}$$
$$20 \times 0.1 = 2 \times (10 \times 0.1) = \underline{\quad}$$
$$100 \times 0.1 = 10 \times \left(\underline{\quad}\right) = \underline{\quad}$$

More awkward multiplications can be handled by changing to 10^{ths}, 100^{ths}, etc. For example

$$\frac{1}{50} = \frac{(1 \times 2)}{(50 \times 2)} = \frac{2}{100} = 2 \times \frac{1}{100}$$

$$\therefore \frac{1}{2} \times \frac{1}{50} = \frac{1}{2} \times \left(2 \times \frac{1}{100}\right) = \underline{\quad}$$

and in decimals, $0.5 \times 0.02 = \underline{\quad}$

Problem 0

> **0** Sometimes an awkward-looking multiplication is easier than it looks because a basic multiplication fact is hidden inside it.
>
> **a** Think how you could work these out *in your head*. Give each answer as a fraction.
>
> **i** $\frac{1}{4} \times \frac{1}{25} = \frac{1}{4} \times \frac{\square}{100} = \frac{1}{\square}$ $\frac{1}{5} \times \frac{1}{20} = \frac{1}{5} \times \frac{\square}{100} = \frac{1}{\square}$
>
> **ii** $\frac{1}{2} \times \frac{1}{500} = \frac{1}{2} \times \frac{\square}{1000} = \frac{1}{\square}$ $\frac{1}{4} \times \frac{1}{250} = \frac{1}{5} \times \frac{1}{200} = \frac{1}{\square}$
>
> **iii** $\frac{1}{20} \times \frac{1}{50} = \frac{1}{\square}$ $\frac{1}{25} \times \frac{1}{40} = \frac{1}{8} \times \frac{1}{125} = \frac{1}{\square}$

b Give each answer as a decimal.

i $0.2 \times 0.05 \quad = \dfrac{2}{\square} \times \dfrac{5}{\square} =$

or $0.2 \times 0.05 = (2 \div 10) \times (5 \div 100) = (2 \times 5) \div 1000 =$

ii $0.25 \times 0.4 \quad =$

iii $0.02 \times 0.5 \quad =$

iv $0.4 \times 0.25 \quad =$

1 Write the decimals for these fractions as efficiently as possible (that is, using cancellation without evaluating the numerator and denominator first).

a $\dfrac{6}{15 \times 20} =$

c $\dfrac{21}{375 \times 8} =$

b $\dfrac{45}{12 \times 75} =$

2 Use the ideas from problem **0** to work out the answers to these multiplications *in your head*.

a $20 \times \dfrac{1}{100} = 2 \times \underline{\quad} =$

b $40 \times 2.5 = 4 \times \underline{\quad} =$

c $60 \times \dfrac{1}{25} = 60 \times \dfrac{\square}{100} =$

d $30 \times 0.01 = 3 \times \underline{\quad} =$

e $\dfrac{2}{5} \times \dfrac{1}{40} = (4 \times \underline{\quad}) \times \dfrac{1}{40} =$

f $0.6 \times 0.05 =$

g $\dfrac{1}{4} \times \dfrac{1}{20} =$

h $0.2 \times 0.15 \quad =$

i $\dfrac{3}{25} \times \dfrac{1}{60} \quad =$

j $0.12 \times 0.025 =$

k $\dfrac{2}{5} \times \dfrac{1}{400} \quad =$

l $1.25 \times 0.08 \quad =$

m $\dfrac{5}{8} \times \dfrac{1}{625} \quad =$

n $6.25 \times 0.0016 =$

3 Use the same ideas to work out the answers to these multiplications in your head.

a $\dfrac{5}{4} \times \dfrac{3}{125} =$

c $\dfrac{3}{25} \times \dfrac{1}{120} =$

b $\dfrac{7}{8} \times \dfrac{3}{875} =$

T24 Prime numbers

'Prime numbers are the very atoms of arithmetic. The primes are those indivisible numbers that cannot be written as two smaller numbers multiplied together. Their importance comes from their power to build all other numbers. Every number that is not a prime can be constructed by multiplying together these prime building blocks. Every molecule in the physical world can be built out of atoms in the periodic table of chemical elements. A list of primes is the mathematician's own periodic table. The prime numbers 2, 3 and 5 are the hydrogen, helium and lithium of the mathematician's laboratory.'

(Marcus du Sautoy, *The Music of the Primes*)

The integer 1 is special: multiplying by 1 has no effect

$$2 = 2 \times 1 = 2 \times 1 \times 1 = \ldots$$

So *1 is a factor of every integer.*

The integer 0 is also special since *every integer is a factor of 0*:

$$0 = 0 \times 0 = 0 \times 1 = 0 \times 1 \times 1 = 0 \times 1 \times 1 \times 1$$
$$= 0 \times 2 = 0 \times 3 = 0 \times 4 = \ldots$$

0 and 1 are not building blocks for larger integers, so they are *not* prime numbers. We concentrate on integers ≥ 2.

Problem 0

---

0 Write the ten integers from 80 to 89 in a single row.

                             80 81 82 83 84 85 86 87 88 89

Cross out all multiples of 2   8̶0̶ 81 8̶2̶ 83 8̶4̶ 85 8̶6̶ 87 8̶8̶ 89

then cross out any remaining multiples of 3

then cross out any remaining multiples of 5

then cross out any remaining multiples of 7.

Circle the integers that remain uncrossed.

None of the circled integers has 2, or 3, or 5, or 7 as a factor.

i How do you know *without checking* that none of the circled numbers is divisible by 4?
For the same reason, none of the circled numbers has 6 or 8 as a factor.

ii How do you know *without checking* that none of the circled numbers is divisible by 9?

---

iii Hence the circled numbers cannot have 2, or 3, or 4, or 5, or 6, or 7, or 8, or 9 as a factor, so the smallest possible factor of any circled number must be ≥ ___.
   This means that the circled numbers cannot be factorised at all! (Why not?) So the circled numbers are all ∗∗i∗e ∗u∗∗e∗∗, and are the only prime numbers in the 80s.

1 Write the integers 90–99 in a row.   90 91 92 93 94 95 96 97 98 99

   Cross out all multiples of 2; then cross out any remaining multiples of 3; then cross out any remaining multiples of 5; then cross out any remaining multiples of 7.

   Circle the integer(s) that remain uncrossed.

   None of the circled integers has 2, or 3, or 5, or 7 as a factor.

   i   How do you know *without checking* that none of the circled numbers is divisible by 4? For the same reason, none of the circled numbers has 6 or 8 as a factor.

   ii How do you know *without checking* that none of the circled numbers is divisible by 9?

   iii Hence the circled numbers cannot have 2, or 3, or 4, or 5, or 6, or 7, or 8, or 9 as a factor, so the smallest possible factor of any circled number must be ≥ ___.
       This means that the circled numbers cannot be factorised at all! (Why not?) So the circled number(s) are all ∗∗i∗e ∗u∗∗e∗∗, and are the only prime numbers in the 90s.

2 Write the integers 100–109 in a row.   100 101 102 103 104 105 106 107 108 109

   Cross out the multiples of 2; then cross out any remaining multiples of 3; then cross out any remaining multiples of 5; then cross out any remaining multiples of 7.

   Circle the integer(s) that remain uncrossed.

   None of the circled integers has 2, or 3, or 5, or 7 as a factor.

   i   How do you know *without checking* that none of the circled numbers is divisible by 4? For the same reason, none of the circled numbers has 6, or ___, or ___ as a factor.

   ii How do you know *without checking* that none of the circled numbers is divisible by 9?

   iii Hence the circled numbers cannot have 2, or 3, or ___, or ___, or ___, or ___, or ___, or ___, or ___ as a factor; so the smallest possible factor of any circled numbers must be ≥ ___.
       This means that the circled numbers cannot be factorised at all! (Why not?) So the circled numbers are all ∗∗i∗e ∗u∗∗e∗∗.

3 Write out the integers from 2 to 99 in ten columns as shown here.

a *Circle the first integer 2, then cross out all larger integers which have 2 as a factor. (Can you see how to do this with just five strokes of the pencil?)*

			②	3	4	5	6	7	8	9
10	11	12	13	14	15	16	17	18	19
20	21	22	23	24	25	26	27	28	29
30	31	32	33	34	35	36	37	38	39
40	41	42	43	44	45	46	47	48	49
50	51	52	53	54	55	56	57	58	59
60	61	62	63	64	65	66	67	68	69
70	71	72	73	74	75	76	77	78	79
80	81	82	83	84	85	86	87	88	89
90	91	92	93	94	95	96	97	98	99

b The smallest uncircled integer which has not been crossed out *has no smaller factor,*
∴ it must be a **i*e *u**e*.

Circle this number, then cross out all larger integers which have this circled number as a factor. (Can you see how to do this with just six strokes of the pencil?)

c The smallest uncircled integer that has not been crossed out has no smaller factor, ∴ it must be a **i*e *u**e*.

Circle this number, then cross out all larger integers which have this circled number as a factor. (Can you see how to do this with just two strokes of the pencil?)

d The smallest uncircled integer which has not been crossed out has no smaller factor, ∴ it must be a **i*e *u**e*.

Circle this number, then cross out all larger integers which have this circled number as a factor. (Can you see how to do this with just four strokes of the pencil?)

e Put a | box | round each of the integers in your table that remain uncircled and which have not yet been crossed out.
None of these integers has 2, or 3, or 5, or 7 as a factor.
How can you be sure *without checking* that none of the boxed integers has 4, or 6, or 8 as a factor?
How can you be sure *without checking* that none of the boxed integers has 9 as a factor?
∴ The smallest possible factor of any the boxed integers is ≥ ___.
∴ None of the boxed integers can be factorised. Explain.
∴ All the boxed integers must all be **i*e *u**e**.

f Make a list of all the prime numbers ≤100.

   i How many prime numbers are there ≤25?

   ii How many prime numbers are there ≤50?

   iii How many prime numbers are there ≤75?

   iv How many prime numbers are there ≤100?

   v What percentage of the positive integers ≤25 are prime numbers?

   vi What percentage of the positive integers ≤50 are prime numbers?

   vii What percentage of the positive integers ≤75 are prime numbers?

   viii What percentage of the positive integers ≤100 are prime numbers?

4 Now repeat problem **3** for integers from 2 to 199, this time putting the integers in twenty columns as shown below.

   a *Circle the first integer* 2, then cross out all larger integers which have 2 as a factor. (Can you see how to do this with just ten strokes of the pencil?)

```
  .  .  ②  3  4  5  6  7  8  9 10 11 12 13 14 15 16 17 18 19
 20 21 22 23 24 25 26 27 28 29 30 31 32 33 34 35 36 37 38 39
 40 41 42 43 44 45 46 47 48 49 50 51 52 53 54 55 56 57 58 59
 60 61 62 63 64 65 66 67 68 69 70 71 72 73 74 75 76 77 78 79
 80 81 82 83 84 85 86 87 88 89 90 91 92 93 94 95 96 97 98 99
100  .  .  .  .  .  .  .  .  .  .  .  .  .  .  .  .  .  .  .
120  .  .  .  .  .  .  .  .  .  .  .  .  .  .  .  .  .  .  .
140  .  .  .  .  .  .  .  .  .  .  .  .  .  .  .  .  .  .  .
160  .  .  .  .  .  .  .  .  .  .  .  .  .  .  .  .  .  .  .
180  .  .  .  .  .  .  .  .  .  .  .  .  .  .  .  . .199
```

   b The smallest uncircled integer that has not been crossed out (namely 3) *has no smaller factor*, so it must be a **i*e *u**e*.

   Circle this number, then cross out all larger integers which have this circled number as a factor. (Can you see how to do this with just ten strokes of the pencil?)

   c The smallest uncircled integer that has not been crossed out (namely 5) *has no smaller factor*, so it must be a **i*e *u**e*.

   Circle this number, then cross out all larger integers which have this circled number as a factor. (Can you see how to do this with just four strokes of the pencil?)

d The smallest uncircled integer that has not been crossed out (namely ___) *has no smaller factor*, so it must be a **i*e *u**e*.

Circle this number, then cross out all larger integers which have this circled number as a factor. (Can you see how to do this with just four strokes of the pencil?)

e The smallest uncircled integer that has not been crossed out (namely ___) *has no smaller factor*, so it must be a **i*e *u**e*.

Circle this number, then cross out all larger integers which have this circled number as a factor.

f The smallest uncircled integer that has not been crossed out (namely ___) *has no smaller factor*, so it must be a **i*e *u**e*.

Circle this number, then cross out all larger integers which have this circled number as a factor.

g Put a [box] round each of the integers in your table that remain uncircled and which have not yet been crossed out. None of these integers has 2, or 3, or 5, or 7, or ___ or ___ as a factor.

How can you be sure *without checking* that none of the boxed integers can have 4, or 6, or ___, or ___, or ___, or ___ as a factor; and none can have ___ as a factor?

∴ The smallest possible factor of any these integers is ≥ ___.
Explain why this means that none of the boxed integers can be factorised, and so must all be **i*e *u**e**.

h Make a list of all the prime numbers ≤200.

   i How many prime numbers are there ≤125?

   ii How many prime numbers are there ≤150?

   iii How many prime numbers are there ≤175?

   iv How many prime numbers are there ≤200?

   v What percentage of the positive integers ≤125 are prime numbers?

   vi What percentage of the positive integers ≤150 are prime numbers?

   vii What percentage of the positive integers ≤175 are prime numbers?

   viii What percentage of the positive integers ≤200 are prime numbers?

T25 What's my number? NC

These problems are not hard, but you are unlikely to know any quick way of solving them. Your job is to use simple arithmetic and systematic searching and calculation to find all possible solutions *without guessing*. There may be more than one answer – so keep alert.

Problem 0

0 I am thinking of a number less than 100. When divided by 6 the remainder is 2. When divided by 5 the remainder is 4.

  a Suppose I tell you that the sum of its digits is odd. Could you tell me my number?

  b Suppose I tell you that the sum of its digits is even. Could you tell me my number?

1 I am thinking of a number less than 100. My number is a multiple of 7, its digits add to 10 and it is odd. What is my number?

2 I am thinking of a number between 20 and 30. When divided by 3, the remainder is 2.

  a Suppose the sum of the digits is even. What can you tell me about my number?

  b Suppose the sum of the digits is odd. What can you tell me about my number?

3 I am thinking of a number less than 50. It is a multiple of 7 and its digits differ by 2. What is my number?

4 I am thinking of a number between 20 and 100. The sum of its digits is a prime number, and the original number is an exact multiple of this prime number.
How many such numbers are there?

5 I am thinking of a number between 20 and 100. When divided by 7 the remainder is 3. When divided by 5 the remainder is 2. What is my number?

6 I am thinking of a number less than 100. It is a multiple of 7 and its digits differ by 1. What is my number?

7 I am thinking of a number less than 100. When divided by 8 the remainder is 5. When divided by 3 the remainder is 1. The sum of its digits is an odd number. What is my number?

TASTER

8 I am thinking of a number less than 100. When divided by 4 the remainder is 2. When divided by 9 the remainder is 5. Its digits differ by 2. What is my number?

9 I am thinking of a number less than 100. When divided by 4 the remainder is 3. When divided by 3 the remainder is 1. The sum of its digits is not divisible by any odd number (other than 1). How many such numbers are there?

10 I am thinking of a number less than 100 with exactly four factors, all of which are odd. The sum of its digits is twice the difference between the digits. What is my number?

11 If everyone gets five apples, there will be six left over. If everyone gets six apples, there will be five left over.
How many people are there?
How many apples are there?

12 Find four integers whose sum is 400, and such that the first integer is equal to twice the second, three times the third, and four times the fourth integer.

13 a Find five consecutive integers such that the sum of the squares of the first three is equal to the sum of the squares of the last two.

    b Is your solution to part **a** the only possible solution?

T26 Area and perimeter problems with rectangles

Problem 0

0 What fraction of this 4 × 1 rectangle is shaded?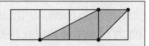

1 Find the area and perimeter of the shape shown here.

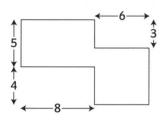

3 Find the perimeter and area of this figure (made from four congruent rectangles)?

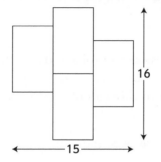

5 What fraction of this rectangle is shaded?

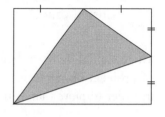

2 This figure is made from a square and two triangles. Find its area.

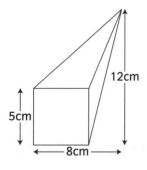

4 This double staircase is made from nine equal squares. Its perimeter is 128 cm. Find its area.

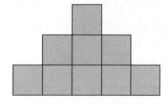

6 What fraction of this regular hexagon is shaded?

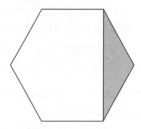

7 What fraction of this regular octagon is shaded?

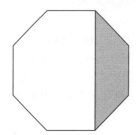

T27 Divisibility *A*: Does it go? **NC**
How do you know?

Problem 0

0 a *Without carrying out the division*, write down the remainder when you divide each of these integers by 10.

i 94	remainder ___	**iv** 345	remainder ___
ii 23 458	remainder ___	**v** 123 456	remainder ___
iii 1 234 321	remainder ___	**vi** 23 454	remainder ___

b How can you tell whether a given integer *N* is divisible by 10? Justify your claim.

There should be no difficulty in answering problem **0a**, or the first part of problem **0b**. However, it may not be clear what to say, or to write, in order to *prove* that your answer to problem **0b** is correct.

Answer
An integer is a multiple of 10 *precisely when* the units digit is 0.

The above answer is probably more precise than you anticipated, so read it again *slowly* to see exactly what it says (and how it says it).

It is true – but *not* enough – to say
　'A given integer is a multiple of 10 if its units digit is 0.'
To understand why this is not enough, consider the statement:
　'An integer is a multiple of 5 if its units digit is 0.'
This is also true – but clearly not the whole truth!

The *answer* above uses the words '*precisely when*' to compress two statements into one:
　'If the units digit is 0, then the integer is a multiple of 10
　and if the units digit is *not* 0, then the integer is *not* a multiple of 10.'

More precisely, when you divide an integer by 10, the units digit tells you the *∗e∗ai∗∗e∗*.

$$30 \quad = 3 \times 10 \therefore \text{ remainder } 0$$
$$140 \quad = 1 \times 100 + 4 \times 10 = 10 \times 10 + 4 \times 10 = 14 \times 10 \therefore \text{ remainder } 0$$
$$37 \quad = 3 \times 10 + 7 \therefore \text{ remainder } 7$$
$$1236 = 1 \times 1000 + 2 \times 100 + 3 \times 10 + 6 = 123 \times 10 + 6 \therefore \text{ remainder } 6$$

1 a *Without carrying out the division*, write down the remainder when you divide each of these integers by 5.

 i 94

 ii 23 458

 iii 1 234 321

 iv 345

 v 123 456

 vi 23 454

 b How can you tell whether a given integer N is divisible by 5? Prove your claim.

Your answer to the first part of problem **1b** must capture *both* parts of your claim 'A given integer is a multiple of 5 *precisely when* its units digit is ___ or ___.'

If the units digit is ___, then the given integer is actually a multiple of 10, so it is automatically a multiple of ___.

If the units digit is ___, then the given integer is a multiple of 10 with remainder 5, and so it is again a multiple of 5.

If on the other hand, the units digit is neither ___ nor ___, then division by 5 leaves a remainder equal to *the remainder you get when you divide the units digit by 5*.

For example
$$1236 = 123 \times 10 + 6 = 123 \times (2 \times 5) + 6$$
$$= 246 \times 5 + (5 + 1) \therefore \text{remainder } \mathbf{1}.$$

2 a *Without carrying out the division*, write down the remainder when you divide each of these integers by 2.

 i 94

 ii 23 458

 iii 1 234 321

 iv 345

 v 123 456

 vi 23 454

 b How can you tell whether a given integer N is divisible by 2? Prove your claim.

Having completed problems **0–2** you certainly know how to tell easily when an integer is divisible by 2, by 5, and by 10.
The next two problems look at divisibility by 4 and by 8. The answers to problems **0, 1** and **2** are probably so familiar that it may have seemed unnecessary to prove what you already know so well. But it is important to understand the logic in problems **0–2** and to try to see how to extend it to the next two problems.

3 a *Without carrying out the division*, write down the remainder when you divide each of these integers by 4.

i	94	**iv**	345
ii	23 458	**v**	123 456
iii	1 234 321	**vi**	23 454

b How can you tell whether a given integer *N* is divisible by 4? Prove your claim.

4 a *Without carrying out the division*, write down the remainder when you divide each of these integers by 8.

i	94	**iv**	345
ii	23 458	**v**	123 456
iii	1 234 321	**vi**	23 454

b How can you tell whether a given integer *N* is divisible by 8? Prove your claim.

We return to these questions in Section C39, where we shall discover how to tell whether an integer is divisible by 3, by 6, or by 9.

T28 Skittles

Joshua rolls one ball at six skittles – numbered 1, 2, 3, 4, 5, 6.
His total score is the sum of the values of the skittles he
knocks down.

Question: How many different ways are there to score a total of 8?

To answer this question accurately, you must list all possibilities
without missing any. So you need a reliable method.

For example, you could make a list of all possible ways of scoring 8,
     first listing ways where *the largest single score* is 6
     then listing ways where *the largest single score* is 5, and so on.

     If 6 is the largest single score, then 8 = 6 + ___: 1 way
     if 5 is the largest single score, then 8 = 5 + ___, or 8 = 5 + ___ + ___: 2 ways
     if 4 is the largest single score, then . . . : ___ way
     3 cannot be the largest single score (or the total score would be at most 3 + 2 + 1 = 6).
     Hence there are altogether just ___ways of getting a total score of 8.

Problem 0

> **0 a i** What is the largest possible 'total score'?
>   How many ways are there to achieve this score?
>
>   **ii** What is the smallest possible 'total score'?
>   How many ways are there to achieve this score?
>
> **b** How many different ways are there to achieve a total score of 10?

1 How many different ways are there to achieve a total score of

  a 1   **c** 3   **e** 5   **g** 7   **i** 9   **k** 11   **m** 13   **o** 15   **q** 17   **s** 19
  b 2   **d** 4   **f** 6   **h** 8   **j** 10 **l** 12   **n** 14   **p** 16   **r** 18   **t** 20

2 a Make a table.

Total score	0	1	2	3	4	5	6	7	8	9	10	11	12	13	14	15	16	17	18	19	20	21
Number of ways																						

> **b** If you have completed the table in part **a** correctly, you should
> notice something unexpected about the second row.
>
> **c** Now add up all the numbers in the second row of the table in
> part **a**. If you have completed the table correctly, you may
> notice something about this total.
>
> We shall come back to parts **b** and **c** later.

C1 Averages: Use your loaf   NC

The place value system we use for numbers makes calculation easy if you 'use your loaf'. For example,

once you know '2 + 3 = ___', you can work out 12 + 3:

(12 = 10 + 2; so 12 + 3 = 10 + (2 + 3) = ___)

Problem **0a** and problem **1** introduce this simple idea, which is then used in the remaining problems to calculate averages.

Problem 0

0 a 3 + 5 = ___ , and 5 + 8 = ___ .
Use these simple facts to spot the answers to these more awkward-looking sums.

  i   13 + 15 =   **iii** 53 + 85 =

  ii 33 + 55 =   **iv** 5353 + 8535 =

  b The average of 3 and 5 is ___ .
Use this to write down the averages of

  i   33 and 55   **iii** 333 and 555

  ii 35 and 53   **iv** 3553 and 5335

1 It is a known *fact* that '2 + 5 = ___ '.
Use this fact to write down each answer *by thinking*: do not work it out the long way.

  a 2 + 15   **d** 502 + 1205   **g** 2222 + 5555

  b 2 + 105   **e** 25 + 52   **h** 2525 + 5252

  c 12 + 105   **f** 205 + 502

2 a Work out the average (that is, the *mean*) of the three numbers, 2, 4, 9.

  b Use your answer to part **a** to find the average of each of these triples by thinking, not by calculating each one directly.

  i   32, 34, 39   **vii**   2002, 4004, 9009

  ii   20, 40, 90   **viii** 22, 44, 99

  iii 982, 984, 989   **ix**   42, 54, 69

  iv   200, 400, 900   **x**   32, 44, 89

  v   1002, 1004, 1009   **xi**   12, 44, 109

  vi   1002, 2004, 3009   **xii**   32, 54, 109

3 a Find the average of each triple of numbers.

   i 79, 80, 81   **iii** 50, 53, 47   **v** 53, 57, 55

   ii 28, 30, 32   **iv** 79, 61, 70   **vi** 99, 88, 110

---

b Find the average of each triple of numbers.

   i 52, 59, 60   **iii** 51, 59, 58

   ii 53, 55, 60   **iv** 58, 42, 56

Problem **3ai** should have been easy, for example,

$79 = 80 - 1, 81 = 80 + 1$, so these balance out, giving 'average = ___'.

Problem **3bi** is harder. For example, you can 'see' that the average of 52, 59 and 60 must be 'a bit less than 59'; the difficult bit is to decide *how much less*.

Think of each number as '$59 \pm$ something':

$52 = 59 - 7, 59 = 59 + 0, 60 = 59 + 1$

$\therefore$ total $= 52 + 59 + 60 = 3 \times 59 - 6 = 3 \times (59 - 2) = 3 \times 57$.

So the average of 52, 59 and 60 must be **57**.

Now use this idea (and your loaf!) to find the averages of the following sets of numbers.

4 a 75, 79, 83   **f** 79, 183, 287

  b 79, 83, 87   **g** 75, 81, 90

  c 78, 80, 85   **h** 77, 83, 92

  d 175, 179, 183   **i** 77, 84, 94

  e 179, 275, 383   **j** 184, 277, 394

5 Look at this list of integers.

    54,   65,   61,   58,   49,   73,   67.

First make a rough guess at the average. Then, by balancing the (positive and negative) differences from your guess, find the true average.

6 The sum of five consecutive integers is equal to 185. What is the smallest of the five integers?

7 In a scout troop there are nine children who each weigh 24 kg, there are three children who each weigh 26 kg and there are two children who each weigh 28 kg. What is the average weight of the complete group?

8 Spiders have 8 legs, ants have 6 legs, mice have 4 legs. 100 creatures have 500 legs. How many more mice must there be than spiders?

C2 Parallel lines and alternate angles

Problem 0

0 You are given two parallel lines linked by a zig-zag of two line segments *AB* and *BC*. Two angles are as shown. How big is the angle marked *x*? Justify your answer.

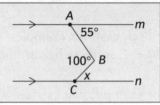

If you rotate a line through 360° about a point, the line returns to its original position *pointing in the same direction*. If you rotate a line through $\frac{1}{2} \times 360° = 180°$ about a point, the line lands up *parallel* to itself *pointing in the opposite direction*.

Imagine two parallel lines *m*, *n* crossed by a third line ℓ, which meets the line *m* at *A* and the line *n* at *B*. Mark the mid-point *M* of the line segment *AB*. Now rotate the figure through 180° about the point *M*. The point *M* stays where it is; the line ℓ lands up on top of itself pointing in the o**o*i*e direction; the point *A* lands up at ___ (since *MA* = *MB*) and the line *m* passing through *A* lands up on top of the parallel line *n* passing through *B* (and pointing in the o**o*i*e direction). The angle marked *x* lands up on top of the angle marked *x'*, so these two angles are *equal*. Whenever two parallel lines are crossed by a third line, angles positioned like *x* and *x'* are said to form a pair of **alternate** angles.

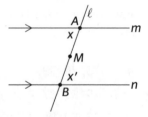

Fact 1 If two lines *m*, *n* are parallel, alternate angles *x* and *x'* are equal.

In fact more is true. *If* two lines *m*, *n* are crossed by a third line ℓ, which meets *m* at *A* and *n* at *B* in such a way that the marked angles *x*, *x'* are equal, *then* *m* and *n* are parallel.
To see why, mark the mid-point *M* of the line segment *AB* and rotate the whole figure through 180° about the point *M*. Then *M* stays exactly where it is, the line ℓ lands up on top of itself pointing in the o**o*i*e direction, the point *A* lands up at ___ (since *MA* = *MB*), and the angle marked *x* fits exactly on top of the angle marked *x'*. So the line *m* passing through the point *A* lands up exactly on top of the line *n* passing through the point *B* (but pointing in the o**o*i*e direction). Hence *m* is *parallel* to *n*.

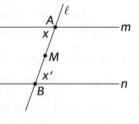

Fact 2 If two lines *m*, *n* are cut by a third line ℓ so that *alternate* angles *x*, *x'* are equal, then the lines *m*, *n* are parallel.

The most important consequence of these two facts concerns the sum of angles in any triangle. Fill in the details in the proof in problem **1**.

1 Claim The angles in any triangle *PQR* add to 180°.

Proof

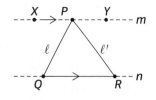

Construct the line *m* = *XPY* through the vertex
P such that *XPY* is ∗a∗a∗∗e∗ to *n* = *QR*.
The line ℓ = *QP* crosses *m* and *n*.
∴ ∠*XPQ* = ∠*RQP* (a∗∗e∗∗a∗e angles)
and the line ℓ′ = *RP* crosses *m* and *n*.
∴ ∠*YPR* = ∠*QRP* (_____ angles)
∴ ∠*RQP* + ∠*QPR* + ∠*QRP* = ∠*XPQ* + ∠*QPR* + ∠*YPR*
          = ∠*XPY* = ___°
          (∠*XPY* is a ∗∗∗ai∗∗∗ a∗∗∗e)   **QED**

In problems **2** and **3** you must draw your own sketch diagram.

2 Claim Given a line *m* and a point *P* not on *m*, there is at most one perpendicular from *P* to *m*.

Proof

Suppose there are two perpendiculars from *P* to *m*, meeting
m at the points *Q* and *R*.
Then ∠*PQR* + ∠*PRQ* = ___° + ___° = 180°.
∴ ∠*QPR* = ___° (since the angles in △*PQR* add to ___°)
∴ *Q* = *R*   **QED**

3 *A*, *B*, *C* lie on the circle with centre *O* such that *OC*∥*AB*.
   If ∠*AOB* = 50°, find ∠*OCB*.

Before returning to tackle more problems in the spirit of problem **0**, we use the result of problem **1** to prove the corresponding result for quadrilaterals: fill in the details in the proof in problem **2**.

4 Claim The angles in any quadrilateral *ABCD* add
   to ___°.

Proof

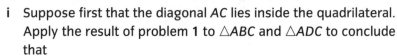

The diagonal *AC* either

   i lies *inside* the quadrilateral *ABCD*, or

   ii lies *outside* the quadrilateral *ABCD*.

i Suppose first that the diagonal *AC* lies inside the quadrilateral.
   Apply the result of problem **1** to △*ABC* and △*ADC* to conclude
   that

      the angles in the quadrilateral *ABCD* add
      to ___° + ___° = ___°.

ii Suppose next that the diagonal *AC* lies outside the quadrilateral. You may assume that *D* lies inside △*ABC*: (if *D* lies outside △*ABC*, then *B* lies inside △*ADC* and we can change the names of the points *B*, *D*).

If we denote the four *internal* angles in the quadrilateral *ABCD* by ∠*A*, ∠*B*, ∠*C*, ∠*D*, then

$$\angle A = \angle BAC - \angle DAC, \angle C = \angle BCA - \angle DCA, \text{ and}$$
$$\angle D = 360° - \angle ADC$$

where ∠*ADC* is the angle at the point *D* in △*ADC*.

∴ ∠*A* + ∠*B* + ∠*C* + ∠*D* = (∠*BAC* − ∠*DAC*) + ∠*B* + (∠*BCA* − ∠*DCA*) + (360° − ∠*ADC*)

= 360° + (∠*BAC* + ∠*BCA* + ∠*B*) − (∠*DAC* + ∠*DCA* + ∠*ADC*)

= ___ °   **QED**

A quadrilateral with four right angles is called a **rectangle**.

5 **Claim** In a rectangle *ABCD*, *AB*∥*DC* and *AD*∥*BC*. Hence ∠*BAC* = ∠*DCA*, ∠*BCA* = ∠*DAC*. (Extend the side *AB* to a point *X*. Then explain why ∠*XBC* = ∠*DCB*. Then use **Fact 2**.)

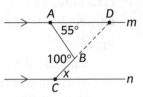

Any full solution to problem **0** must use properties of alternate angles. The solution below is provided to show one way to approach the next set of problems.

Solution

Extend the line segment *CB* to meet the line *m* passing through *A* at the point *D*.

∴ ∠*ABD* = 180° − ∠*ABC* = ___   (*CBD* is a ***ai*** a****e)

∴ ∠*ADB* = 180° − (∠*DAB* + ∠*ABD*)   (angles in △*ABD*)

= ___

∴ *x* = ∠*ADB*   (a**e**a*e a***e*)

= ___

6 In each figure calculate the angle marked '?' in terms of the given angles.

a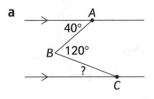

b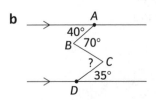

c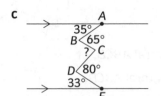

d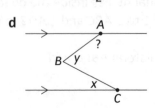

e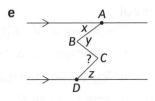

7 Let *ABCD* be a rhombus (that is, a quadrilateral with *AB* = *BC* = *CD* = *DA*). Draw your own diagram and justify each step in the following two proofs.

    a   ∠*BAD* = ∠*BAC* + ∠*CAD*

              = ∠*BCA* + ∠*CAD* (△*BAC* is _____ with *BA* = *BC*)

              = ∠*BCA* + ∠*ACD* (△ ___ is _____ with ___ = ___)

              = ∠*BCD*

      ∴ The angles at opposite corners *A*, *C* of a rhombus *ABCD* are
        equal.   **QED**

    b   ∠*ABC* = ∠*ADC*   (the angles at ___ corners of a rhombus are ___ .)

        ∠*ABC* + 2 × ∠*BAC* = ___ (Problem **1** applied to the i*o**e*e* △*ABC*)

        ∠*ADC* + 2 × ∠*DCA* = ___ (Problem **1** applied to the i*o**e*e* △*DAC*)

           ∴   ∠*BAC* = ___

           ∴   *AB* ∥ *DC*   (___ angles equal)

      Similarly   *AD* ∥ *BC*

      ∴ Opposite sides of a rhombus are parallel.   **QED**

8 Let *ABCD* be a rhombus. Produce *AB* to *R*. Let *BS* bisect ∠*RBC*. Prove that *BS*∥*AC*.

A quadrilateral *ABCD* in which each pair of opposite sides are parallel (that is, *AB*∥*DC* and *AD*∥*BC*) is called a **parallelogram.**

9 Let *ABCD* be a quadrilateral in which *AB*∥*DC* and *AB* = *BD* = *DC*. Prove that *AD*∥*BC*.

10 **a** Let *ABCD* be a parallelogram.
       Prove that the angles at opposite corners are equal.

    b Let *ABCD* be a quadrilateral in which each pair of angles at opposite corners are equal.
       Prove that *ABCD* is a parallelogram.

11 Let *ABCD* be a parallelogram. Produce *AB* to *X* such that *BX* = *BC* and *BA* to *Y* such that *AY* = *AD*. Join *XC*, *YD* and produce both lines to meet at *O*.
    Find ∠*XOY*.

12 Two parallel lines *m*, *n* are given with a line *ℓ* crossing *m* at *A* and crossing *n* at *B*. The bisectors of the two internal angles at *A* and at *B* on one side of the line *ℓ* meet at *X*.
    Find (with proof) ∠*AXB*.

C3 Multiplication: Integers and decimals   NC

In mathematics you need to be able to calculate quickly and accurately – leaving your mind and your imagination free to think about the *results* of your calculations. In particular, whenever a calculation produces a surprisingly simple exact answer (such as 222 222, or 1), or a suspicious-looking approximation (such as 0.99999996), it is worth pausing to think whether this may be trying to tell you something!

Problem 0

0 **a** Work out 3367×33 laying out your calculation as shown on the right.

```
      3 3 6 7
  ×       3 3
    * * * * *
  * * * * * 0
  * * * * * *
  _____
```

b Work out 7.7×1.3.

First change this to an integer multiplication.

$7.7 \times 1.3 = (7.7 \times 10) \times (1.3 \times 10) \div 100 = (\underline{} \times \underline{}) \div 100$.

Then use long multiplication to multiply the integers.

Finally divide the answer by 100 to obtain the answer to the original problem: $7.7 \times 1.3 = \underline{} \div 100 = \underline{}$

```
      7 7
  ×   1 3
    * * *
    * * 0
    _____
  * * * *
```

Use this standard layout to work out the answers to these decimal calculations. Do *not* use a calculator.

1 $259 \times 429 \quad =$

2 $4.81 \times 0.231 \quad =$

3 $8547 \times 26 \quad =$

4 $0.01443 \times 69.3 =$

5 $529.1 \times 0.0189 =$

6 $28.49 \times 3.51 \quad =$

7 $0.858 \times 103.6 \quad =$

8 $9.009 \times 3.7 \quad =$

9 $245.7 \times 0.0407 =$

10 $0.05439 \times 143 \quad =$

11 Work out all possibilities for the missing digits in these long multiplications. Don't guess! There may be more than one solution. So you must work logically and justify each step to make sure you find all possibilities.

a
```
        * * 6
  ×       * *
      6 * 3 4
    * * * * *
    _____
    * * 6 1 *
```

b
```
        6 *
  ×     * *
        * *
      * * 0
    _____
      * * 6
```

C4 Drawing conclusions *C*: Side-Side-Side congruence

A triangle is more than just a shape – it is a *labelled* shape. The order of the vertices matters. A labelled triangle *ABC* has six parts:

◎ three *sides* (*AB*, *BC*, *CA*), and

◎ three *angles* (the angle ∠*CAB* at the vertex *A*, the angle ∠*ABC* at the vertex *B*, and the angle ∠*BCA* at the vertex *C*).

In this section we show that

SSS: the lengths of the three sides *AB*, *BC*, *CA* are enough to determine the triangle completely.

If the three Sides of one triangle *ABC* are equal to the corresponding Sides of a second triangle *A′B′C′*,

Then the two triangles must be 'equal in all respects', or *congruent*.

This fact is known as the SSS (Side-Side-Side) **congruence criterion** for triangles.

Problem 0

0 a Draw two triangles *ABC* and *A′B′C′* like the ones shown here.
Note that:

(A) ∠*ABC* = ∠*A′B′C′*

(S) *BC* = *B′C′*

(S) *CA* = *C′A′*,

but ∠*ACB* ≠ ∠*A′C′B′*

∴ △*ABC* and △*A′B′C′*
are *not* congruent.

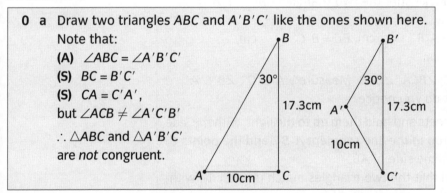

Problem **0a** shows that, if we want to prove that two triangles are congruent, then matching up *any three* pairs of 'parts' is not enough.

On the other hand problem **0b** below will suggest that matching up *three sides* (SSS) is always enough to guarantee that the two triangles are congruent.

Problem 0

0 b Take two loose sheets of A4 paper.

i On the *first* sheet draw (as accurately as you can) a line segment AB with $AB = 17.3$ cm. Label the two end-points A and B.
On the *second* sheet draw (as accurately as you can) a line segment $A'B'$ with $A'B' = 17.3$ cm. Label the two end-points A' and B'.

ii On the *first* sheet mark the point X on the segment AB with $AX = 10$ cm and the point Y on '*BA* produced' with $BY = 20$ cm.
On the *second* sheet mark the point X' on the segment $A'B'$ with $A'X' = 10$ cm and the point Y' on $B'A'$ produced with $B'Y' = 20$ cm.

iii On the *first* sheet draw the circle with centre A and passing through the point X and the circle with centre B and passing through the point Y. Let these two circles cross at the points C and D.
On the *second* sheet draw the circle with centre A' and passing through the point X' and the circle with centre B' and passing through the point Y'. Let these two circles cross at the points C' and D'.

iv Go back and draw in the line segments AB, BC, CA on the first sheet, and the line segments $A'B'$, $B'C'$, $C'A'$ on the second sheet. Make sure the two triangles ABC and $A'B'C'$ stand out clearly.
Note that: $AB = A'B' = \_\_\_$ cm, $BC = B'C' = \_\_\_$ cm, $CA = C'A' = \_\_\_$ cm.

v Measure $\angle ABC$, $\angle BCA$, $\angle CAB$. Measure $\angle A'B'C'$, $\angle B'C'A'$, $\angle C'A'B'$. What do you notice?

vi Take the two sheets and hold them up to the light, with the side AB exactly on top of the line segment $A'B'$, and the points C and C' on the same side of AB.
You should find that the two triangles match up exactly, with
◎ $\angle ABC$ exactly on top of $\angle A'B'C'$
◎ $\angle BCA$ exactly on top of $\angle B'C'A'$
◎ $\angle CAB$ exactly on top of $\angle C'A'B'$.

SSS congruence criterion

Given two triangles $\triangle ABC$ and $\triangle A'B'C'$ with
$AB = A'B'$, $BC = B'C'$, and $CA = C'A'$.
Then the two triangles are identical. In particular, each angle in the first triangle matches the corresponding angle in the second triangle: $\angle ABC = \angle A'B'C'$, $\angle BCA = \angle B'C'A'$, $\angle CAB = \angle C'A'B'$.

1 a Draw AB of length 12 cm. Mark the point X on AB produced with AX = 13 cm and the point Y on BA with BY = 5 cm. Draw the circle with centre A and passing through X and the circle with centre B and passing through Y; let these two circles meet at the point C. Measure ∠ABC. What do you notice?

   b Draw AB of length 6 cm. Mark the point X on AB produced with AX = 14 cm and the point Y on BA produced with BY = 10 cm. Draw the circle with centre A and passing through X and the circle with centre B and passing through Y; let these two circles meet at the point C. Measure ∠ABC. What do you notice?

   c Draw AB of length 8 cm. Mark the point X on AB with AX = 7 cm and the point Y on BA with BY = 5 cm. Draw the circle with centre A and passing through X and the circle with centre B and passing through Y; let these two circles meet at the point C. Measure ∠ABC. What do you notice?

Problems **1a**, **b**, **c** illustrate the SSS congruence criterion and show that sometimes the three side lengths determine unexpectedly 'nice' angles. The remaining problems give you the chance to use SSS to *prove* some important results in elementary geometry.

2 Two circles with centres at A and B meet at C and D. Prove that the line AB joining the centres of the two circles bisects both ∠DAC and ∠DBC.

3 **Given** a line segment BC. Let X be any point that is *equidistant* from B and from C, that is, with XB = XC. Join X to the mid-point M of BC. **Prove** that ∠XMB = ∠XMC = ___°, so that X must lie on the *perpendicular bisector* of the line segment BC.

4 Let ABC be an isosceles triangle with base BC. Let M be the mid-point of BC. Prove that AM is perpendicular to BC and that AM bisects ∠BAC.

Recall that a quadrilateral ABCD is a **rhombus** if AB = BC = CD = DA.

5 Let ABCD be a rhombus.

   a Prove (using only SSS and the above definition of a rhombus) that ∠BAC = ∠DCA.

   b Conclude that

      i AB∥DC and AD∥BC (that is, ABCD is a parallelogram);

      ii AC bisects ∠BAD.

6 Let ABCD be any quadrilateral such that AB = DC and AD = BC. Prove that AB∥DC and AD∥BC, so ABCD is a parallelogram.

The SSS congruence criterion allows us to *prove* that, in any isosceles triangle, the base angles are equal (this was demonstrated *experimentally* in Section T15).

7   **Claim** *The base angles of any isosceles triangle are equal.*
   Proof Let △*ABC* be an isosceles triangle with base *BC* and with apex *A*.
   △*ACB* uses the same three vertices (*A*, *B*, *C*), but is labelled differently,
   so is a different triangle. However, corresponding sides in the two
   differently labelled triangles △*ABC* and △*ACB* match up in pairs.

   (S) *AB* = *AC* (given: we are told that △*ABC* is isosceles with
        base *BC*, so *AB* =*AC*)
   (S) *AC* = *A* ___ (given: same reason)
   (S) *BC* = *CB* (same segment reversed)
   ∴ △*ABC* and △*ACB* are congruent triangles (by the ___ congruence criterion).
   ∴ ∠*ABC* in △*ABC* is equal to the corresponding angle
   ∠*A* ___ in △*ACB*.   **QED**

Since an *equilateral* triangle is an isosceles triangle in three different ways,
one consequence of problem 7 is that in an equilateral triangle all three
angles are equal.
∴ (by **C2**, problem 1) each angle in an equilateral triangle equals ___°.

The same is *not true* for quadrilaterals: a rhombus is most *unlikely* to be a
square! This should remind you that – for polygons with more than
three sides – having equal sides does not make the polygon regular.

8   *A, B, C, D, E* are five points in order *on a circle* with centre *O*.
   If *AB* = *BC* = *CD* = *DE* = *EA*, prove that ∠*ABC* = ∠*BCD* = ∠*CDE* = ∠*DEA*
   = ∠*EAB* , so the pentagon is a regular pentagon.

A quadrilateral *ABCD* with two pairs of adjacent sides equal is a **kite**.

9   Let *ABCD* be a kite with *AB* = *BC* and *CD* = *DA*.

   a Prove that *BD* bisects ∠*ABC* and ∠*ADC*.

   b Let *M* be the mid-point of *AC*. Prove that *BM* bisects ∠*ABC*.
      Conclude that *BD* bisects *AC* and that *BD* is perpendicular to *AC*.

In problem **0a** you were given two triangles in which *one pair of angles*
and *two pairs of sides* matched up exactly, but the two triangles (ASS) were
definitely *not* congruent.
In problem **0b** you saw that if all three sides of two triangles match up
exactly (SSS), then the two triangles have to be congruent.

This raises the question
'Suppose you are given a triangle *ABC*. Which combinations of sides and
angles determine the *exact* shape of the triangle?'

Later sections (**C7, C15**) show that, like SSS, SAS and ASA are also
sufficient to determine the shape of a triangle.

C5 Ruler and compass constructions

CORE

Problem **0** below brings together results about rhombuses that you may have already proved in **C2** and **C4**. They are repeated here because they lie at the heart of the basic *Ruler and Compass* (R&C) constructions.

Problem 0

0 Draw a line segment *AC* of length 8 cm. Draw the circle with centre *A* passing through *C* and the circle with centre *C* passing through *A*. Let these two circles meet at *B* and at *D*.

a Prove that *ABCD* is a rhombus.

b Prove that *AB∥DC* and *AD∥BC*.

c Prove that *AC* bisects ∠*BAD*.

d Mark the mid-point *M* of *AC*. Prove that *BM* bisects ∠*ABC*.
Conclude that *BD* passes through *M*, and that *BD* bisects *AC*.

e Prove that *AC* and *BD* are perpendicular.

Given any two points *X* and *Y*

◎ imagine the ruler as a way of constructing
exactly the line *XY* through the two given points

and

◎ imagine the compasses as a way of constructing
exactly the circle with centre *X* and with the
line segment *XY* as radius.

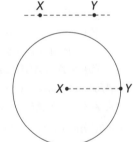

Our own attempts at drawing are inevitably approximate. In contrast, the ruler and compasses in R&C constructions are imaginary instruments, which are used *exactly* to carry out *perfect* constructions *according to the rules of geometry*. Our own imperfect rulers and not-very-sharp pencils must never obscure the spirit underlying ruler and compass constructions: namely that the procedure being followed has to be *exact in principle*.

Since there is no such thing as exact measurement

◎ the ruler must never be used to measure (which is why it is
sometimes referred to as a 'straightedge' or unmarked ruler)

◎ the compasses must never be used as 'dividers' to transfer a line
segment *XY*, or length, from one point *X* to another point *Z*; they
can only be used to carry a given radius *XY around a given centre X*.

The problems that follow make explicit the basic R&C constructions in problem **0** and give you the chance to write out proofs that they do what they claim. These basic constructions are then used to derive other constructions.

1 **Given** ∠BAC.
   Construct a point X such that AX bisects ∠BAC.
   Prove your construction does what you claim it does.

   Construction of the bisector of the given angle ∠BAC
   (Copy and fill in the gaps in the following solution to problem 1.)

   Extend the two arms AB, ___ of the given angle ∠BAC.

   Let the circle with centre A that passes through the point B meet AC (produced if necessary) at B′.
   △ABB′ is i∗o∗∗e∗e∗ (since ___ = ___).

   The two circles:
   i   with centre B and passing through the point A
   ii with centre B′ and passing through the point A
       have equal ∗a∗ii (since ___ = ___).

   Let these two circles meet at the point A′. Draw AA′.

   Claim ∠A′AB = ∠A′AB′ (= ∠A′AC), so AA′ bisects the given angle
           ∠BAC.

   Proof
           (S) AB = AB′ (both a ___ of the same circle with centre ___)
           (S) BA′ = B′A′ (since BA′ = ___, B′A′ = ___, and ___ = ___ by
               the previous step)
           (S) A′A = A′A (same segment)
   ∴ △ABA′ is congruent to △AB′A′ (by the ___ congruence criterion)
   ∴ ∠A′AB = ∠A′AB′, so AA′ bisects ∠BAB′ = ∠BAC.   **QED**

2 Let ABC be an isosceles triangle with base BC. Let M be the mid-point of BC. Use the SSS congruence criterion to prove that AM is perpendicular to BC and that AM bisects ∠BAC.

The next challenge is to justify the familiar R&C construction of the mid-point of a given segment BC. The proof that this construction 'does what it says on the tin' needs a step which we summarise in problem 3.

3 You know (problem **2** above) that, given an isosceles triangle ABC with M the mid-point of the base BC, the line AM is ∗e∗∗e∗∗i∗u∗a∗ to BC.

   But you also know (C2, problem 2) that, given a line m = BC and a point A not on m, there is a∗ ∗o∗∗ o∗e perpendicular from A to m.

   ∴ If in the given isosceles triangle ABC with AB = AC you construct a point X on BC such that AX⊥BC (that is, AX is perpendicular to BC), you can be sure that X = ___.

4 Given a line segment *BC*.

Construct the mid-point *M* of *BC* (without measuring, using ruler and compasses only).

Prove your construction does what you claim it does.

Construction of the mid-point of a given segment BC

(You may already have solved problem **4** as part of problem **0d**. Problem **4** offers the chance to write out a more systematic solution using the results of problems **1**, **2** and **3**. Copy and fill in the gaps in the following solution.)

Draw the line segment *BC* whose *i*-*oi** is to be constructed.   B •————————————• C

Draw the circle C with centre *B* and passing through the point *C* and the circle C' with centre *C* and passing through *B*.
Let these two circles meet at the points *A* and *A'*.

Claim *BC and AA' cross at the mid-point M of the line segment BC.*

Proof

BC and *AA'* must cross, but at this stage we cannot be sure *where*.

Let *X* be the point where the lines *BC*, *AA'* cross.

We use the results of problems **1**, **2** and **3** to show that *X* = *M*.

a First use problem **1** to bisect ∠*BAC*.
The construction takes ∠*BAC* and draws the circle with centre *A* passing through *B*.

   i The circle with centre *A* and passing through the point *B* meets the line *AC* at the point ___ (because *AB* = ___).

   ii The circle with centre *B* and passing through *A* is precisely the circle C above (since *A* and *C* both lie on the circle C). Similarly, the circle with centre *C* and passing through *A* is precisely the circle C' above (since *A* and ___ both lie on the circle C').

   iii These two circles meet at the point ___.
     ∴ ___ bisects ∠*BAC*
     ∴ ∠*BAA'* = ∠___
     ∴ ∠*BAX* = ∠*BAA'* = ∠___ = ∠*CAX*
     ∴ *AX* bisects ∠*BAC* (*).

b But △*ABC* is i*o**e*e* with base *BC*.
  ∴ *AM* bisects ∠*B*___ (by problem **2**).
  ∴ *M* and ___ must be the same point (as in problem **3**).   **QED**

5 Given a line segment *AC*.

Construct the *perpendicular bisector* of the segment *AC* (without measuring, using ruler and compasses only).

Prove your construction does what you claim it does.

6   **Given** a line ℓ and a point M on that line.
    Construct the line which is perpendicular to ℓ and that passes
    through the point M.
    Prove your construction does what you claim it does.
    (Start by drawing a circle with centre M, which meets the line ℓ at points A
    and C. Then M is the *i*-*oi** of AC; so you may proceed as in problem **4**.)

7   **Given** a line ℓ and a point B not on the line ℓ.
    Construct the line which is perpendicular to ℓ and that passes
    through the point B.
    Prove your construction does what you claim it does.
    (Start by drawing a circle with centre B, and passing through
    a point A on the line ℓ. Let this circle meet the line ℓ again
    at the point C. Then proceed as in problem **4**.)

8   **Given** a line ℓ and a point B not on the line ℓ.
    Construct the line through B which is parallel to ℓ.
    Prove your construction does what you claim it does. (First use the
    construction in problem **6** to construct the line m, which passes
    through the point B and which is perpendicular to ℓ. Then use the
    construction in problem **5** to construct the line n through B which
    is perpendicular to m. Finally prove that n is parallel to ℓ.)

9   a   **Given** a line segment AB.
        Construct a point C such that ABC is an equilateral triangle.

    b   **Given** a line segment AB. **Construct** a point C such that
        CB⊥AB and CB = AB. Draw the circle with centre A and
        passing through B and the circle with centre C and
        passing through A; let these two circles meet at the point D.
        Prove that ABCD is a square (that is, that AB = BC = CD = DA
        and ∠ABC = ∠BCD = ∠CDA = ∠DAB).

    c   **Given** a line segment AB.
        Construct C, D, E, F such that ABCDEF is a regular hexagon.
        Prove that ABCDEF is a regular hexagon.

    d   **Given** a line segment AB.
        Construct points C, D, E, F, G, H such that ABCDEFGH is a
        regular octagon.
        Prove that ABCDEFGH is a regular octagon.

10 a   Suppose ∠ABC = 70°. Let D lie on AC produced. Let the bisector
        of ∠BAC meet the bisector of the external angle ∠BCD at X.
        Calculate ∠AXC.

    b   Suppose ∠ABC = b°. Let D lie on AC produced. Let the bisector
        of ∠BAC meet the bisector of the external angle ∠BCD at X.
        Calculate ∠AXC.

Totals

NC

In mathematics you learn how to calculate. But you also need to think. Sometimes a simple idea can help to uncover hidden information in a way that makes calculations easier than they may seem at first sight.

Problem 0

0 A present in a box (a cuboid) is wrapped and tied up with string, with one loop of string in each of the three possible directions (as shown). The total length of string is $T = 108$ cm and the middle one of the three dimensions is the average of the other two dimensions. The volume of the cuboid is 648 cm^3. Find the dimensions of the cuboid.

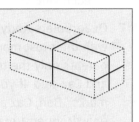

1 Jane, Katy and Louise refused to go on the scales. So the nurse persuaded them to be weighed in pairs instead. Jane and Katy weighed 76 kg together; Katy and Louise weighed 87 kg and Louise and Jane weighed 98 kg. What is the combined weight of all three? And what are their individual weights?

2 Each dart can score either 3 or 5 (or 0 if it misses the target altogether).

   a i   Which scores ≤ 20 cannot be achieved?

   ii Which scores can be achieved, but need more than four darts?

   b Which scores between 20 and 35 need more than seven darts?

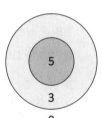

3 Thirty-six people live in the eight houses round *Perfect Square*. Each house has a different number of people living in it. And along each edge of the square, each row of three houses contains fifteen people. How many people live in each house?

4 **a** Zids have five spots, Zods have nine spots. Some Zids and Zods have 74 spots between them. How many Zids are there and how many Zods?

   b Zids have five spots, Zods have nine spots. Some Zids and Zods have 112 spots between them. How many Zids are there and how many Zods?

5 Snow White notices that some of the Dwarfs have put on weight, while others are fading away. So she decides it is time to weigh them all. Bashful, Dopey, Lazy and Sleepy refuse to be weighed separately, but they finally agree to be weighed in threes. Bashful, Dopey and Lazy weigh in at 43 stone; Dopey, Lazy and Sleepy weigh in at 54 stone; Lazy, Sleepy and Bashful weigh in at 65 stone; finally, Sleepy, Bashful and Dopey weigh in at 66 stone. How much does each Dwarf weigh?

6 When the whole family comes to visit we sit down to lunch on chairs and three-legged stools. Suppose all you know is that these seats have 74 legs between them.

   a What is the largest number of people you know we *can be sure* of seating? If this is the actual number of seats, how many seats are there of each kind?

   b What is the largest number of people we *may be able* to seat? If this is the actual number of seats, how many seats are there of each kind?

7 Quadruplets Andy, Ben, Caz and Dwayne were not too pleased with their test marks (out of 30). So they decided to tell their parents only the totals scored by certain threesomes. Andy, Ben and Caz said 'If you combine our scores, then we sort of got full marks.' Ben, Caz and Dwayne said: 'If we do the same, then we only dropped 1 mark.' Caz, Dwayne and Andy said: 'If you add our scores then we were five short of full marks.' Dwayne, Andy and Ben said: 'The total of our three scores was six short of full marks.' What were the four individual scores?

8 In the cuboid *ABCDEFGH* the perimeters of the faces *ABCD*, *ADEF*, *ABGF* are given. Find the length, breadth and height of the cuboid

   a if the three faces have perimeters 8 cm, 10 cm and 12 cm

   b if the three faces have perimeters 12 cm, 14 cm and 16 cm

   c if the three faces have perimeters $11\frac{2}{3}$ cm, $13\frac{1}{2}$ cm, $15\frac{1}{6}$ cm.

9 You are given a cuboid.

   a Suppose the different faces have areas 15 cm^2, 21 cm^2 and 35 cm^2. What is the volume of the cuboid and what are the lengths of the edges?

   b Suppose the different faces have areas $12\frac{1}{2}$ cm^2, 15 cm^2 and 30 cm^2. What is the volume of the cuboid and what are the lengths of the edges?

   c Suppose the different faces have areas $\frac{4}{15}$ cm^2, $\frac{5}{3}$ cm^2 and $\frac{9}{4}$ cm^2. What is the volume of the cuboid and what are the lengths of the edges?

10 You are given a cuboid with volume 600 cm^3 and total surface area 1298 cm^2, and in which the total length of all the edges is 200 cm. Find the dimensions of the cuboid.

C7 Drawing conclusions *D*: Side-Angle-Side congruence

C2

CORE

A triangle is more than just a shape – it is a *labelled* shape. The order of the vertices matters. A labelled triangle *ABC* has six parts:

◎ three *sides* (*AB*, *BC*, *CA*), and

◎ three *angles* (the angle ∠*CAB* at the vertex *A*, the angle ∠*ABC* at the vertex *B*, and the angle ∠*BCA* at the vertex *C*).

In Section **C4** we derived the **SSS congruence criterion** for triangles and raised the question 'Given a triangle *ABC*, which combinations of sides and angles determine the *exact shape* of the triangle?'

In this section we show that

> **SAS**: 'any two Sides together with the Angle *between* them' are enough to determine the triangle *ABC* completely.

If two Sides (say *AB*, *BC*) and the Angle between them (∠*ABC*) in one triangle △*ABC* are equal to the corresponding two Sides (*A′B′*, *B′C′*) and the Angle between them (∠*A′B′C′*) in a second triangle △*A′B′C′*, **then** the two triangles must be 'equal in all respects', or *congruent*.

This is known as the **SAS (Side-Angle-Side) congruence criterion** for triangles.

Problem 0

---

0 Take two loose sheets of A4 paper.

a On the *first* sheet draw (as accurately as you can) a line segment *AB* with *AB* = 8.3 cm. Label the two endpoints *A* and *B*. On the *second* sheet draw (as accurately as you can) a line segment *A′B′* with *A′B′* = 8.3 cm. Label the two end-points *A′* and *B′*.

b On the *first* sheet use a protractor to construct a line *AX* with ∠*BAX* = 54°. Take the *second* sheet and construct a line *A′X′* with ∠*B′A′X′* = 54°.

c Take the *first* sheet and mark the point *C* on the line *AX* with *AC* = 7.5 cm. Take the *second* sheet and mark the point *C′* on the line *A′X′* with *A′C′* = 7.5 cm.

d Go back and draw over the line segments *AB* and *AC* on the first sheet, and the line segments *A′B′* and *A′C′* on the second sheet *so that they both stand out clearly*. Then draw (slightly less boldly) the line segment *BC* on the first sheet and the line segment *B′C′* on the second sheet.

85

e i Measure *BC* and *B'C'*. What do you notice?

ii Measure ∠*ABC* and ∠*A'B'C'*. What do you notice?

iii Measure ∠*ACB* and ∠*A'C'B'*. What do you notice?

f Take the two sheets and hold them up to the light. Make sure

that the line segment *AB* lies exactly on top of the line segment *A'B'*

that the angle ∠*BAC* lies exactly on top of the angle ∠*B'A'C'*

that the line segment *AC* lies exactly on top of the line segment *A'C'*.

Since the point *B* lies exactly on top of the point *B'* and the point *C* lies exactly on top of the point *C'*

the line segment *BC* must lie exactly on top of *B'C'*, so *BC* = *B'C'*

the angle ∠*ABC* must lie exactly on top of ∠*A'B'C'*, so ∠*ABC* = ∠*A'B'C'*

the angle ∠*ACB* must lie exactly on top of ∠*A'C'B'*, so ∠*ACB* = ∠*A'C'B'*.

SAS congruence criterion

Given two triangles △*ABC* and △*A'B'C'*

with *AB* = *A'B'*, ∠*BAC* = ∠*B'A'C'*, and *AC* = *A'C'*

Then the two triangles are identical.

In particular, the third sides of the two triangles are equal: *BC* = *B'C'*, and each of the remaining angles is equal to the corresponding angle in the other triangle:

∠*ABC* = ∠*A'B'C'*, ∠*ACB* = ∠*A'C'B'*.

In the first problem a skeleton solution is provided to indicate how you should write your own solutions.

Copy it and complete the missing parts.

1 Given △*ABC* with *AB* = *AC*.

Prove a The bisector of ∠*BAC* meets *BC* at the midpoint *M* of *BC*.

b ∠*AMB* = ∠*AMC* = 90°.

Solution The bisector of ∠*BAC* must meet *BC* at some point: let us call this point *M*. We want to prove that:

a *BM* = *CM* (from which it follows that *M* is the *i**oi** of *BC*),

and **b** ∠*AMB* = ∠*AMC* (from which it follows that each is half of a ***ai*** angle).

To this end, consider △*AMB* and △*AMC*:

(S) *BA* = ___ (given)

(A) ∠*BAM* = ∠___ (*AM* is the *i*e**o* of ∠ ___)

(S) *AM* = *AM* (same segment)

∴ △*AMB* and △*AMC* are *o***ue** (by the ___ congruence criterion).

∴ *BM* = ___ and ∠*AMB* = ∠ ___ as required. **QED**

2 **Given** C is the centre of both circles. ACB and DCE are straight lines.
Prove $DB = AE$.

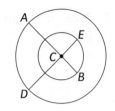

3 **Given** C is the centre of the semicircles OPQ and XYZ. CYP is a radius of the larger semicircle.
Prove $\angle QOY = \angle XPY$.

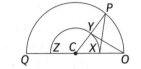

4 **Given** line segments AB and CD cross at M, which is the mid-point of both segments.
Prove $AD = CB$ and $AD \| CB$.

5 **Given** O is the centre of two circles. AB is a chord of the larger circle, and XY is a chord of the smaller circle, such that OXA, OYB are radii of the larger circle.
Prove $\angle XBA = \angle YAB$.

The SAS congruence condition makes it possible to *re-prove* the familiar experimental facts about the base angles of an isosceles triangle. (The basic result was proved in Section **C4** using the **SSS congruence criterion**.) Fill in the missing details in the next three proofs (problems **6** and **7**).

6 **Given** three points A, B, C (not all on a line) with $AB = AC$.
Prove $\angle ABC = \angle ACB$.
Proof 1 Look again at your solution to problem **1**.
There what was 'Given' was exactly the same: $\triangle ABC$ with $AB = AC$. As part of the proof that the bisector of $\angle BAC$ meets BC at its mid-point, we let the bisector of $\angle BAC$ meet BC at some point M and showed that $\triangle AMB$ and $\triangle AMC$ are congruent (whence $MB = MC$, so M is in fact the mid-point of BC).
Use this to conclude that $\angle ABC = \angle ACB$.   **QED**

Proof 2 The three points A, B, C give rise to *i* different 'ordered triangles'.
$\triangle ABC$ and $\triangle ACB$ are two of these ordered triangles:
    (S) $AB = AC$ (given)
    (A) $\angle BAC = \angle CAB$ (same angle)
    (S) $AC = $ ___ (given)
$\therefore \triangle ABC$ and $\triangle ACB$ are *o***ue** (by the ___ congruence criterion)
$\therefore \angle ABC = \angle$ ___.   **QED**

With a little ingenuity one can also prove the converse result – namely: 'if the base angles of a triangle are equal, then the triangle is isosceles.'

7 **Given** three points A, B, C (not all on a line) with $\angle ABC = \angle ACB$.
Prove $AB = AC$.
Proof A, B, C are three points that give rise to *i* different (ordered) triangles.
$\triangle ABC$ and $\triangle ACB$ are two of these ordered triangles.
Suppose $AB \neq AC$, then one is longer – say $AC > AB$.
We can then construct a point D on the segment AC such that $CD = BA$.
Think about the two triangles $\triangle ABC$ and $\triangle DCB$.

   (S) $AB = DC$ (this is how the point D was constructed)
   (A) $\angle ABC = \angle DCB$ ($\angle DCB$ is the same angle as $\angle$ ___ and
      $\angle ABC = \angle$ ___ is given)
   (S) $BC =$ ___ (same line segment)
$\therefore$ $\triangle ABC$ and $\triangle DCB$ are *o***ue** (by the ___ congruence criterion)
$\therefore$ $\angle ACB = \angle DBC < \angle ABC$, which is impossible (since $\angle ACB = \angle ACB$ is given).
$\therefore$ We must have been *wrong* when we said
'Suppose $AB \neq DC$'.   **QED**

Use these two results to solve the next batch of problems. Make sure you draw your own sketch for each problem.

8 $\triangle ABC$ is such that $AB = AC$. X is the point on AB such that $CB = CX$.
If $\angle BAC = 40°$, find $\angle ACX$.

9 A, B, C, D are four points in order on a line. The point E is such that $\angle ABE = 140°$ and $\angle ADE = 35°$. If $BE = BC$, prove that $CE = CD$.

10 In $\triangle ABC$ the bisectors of $\angle ABC$ and $\angle ACB$ meet at I. If $AB = AC$, prove that $IB = IC$.

Recall that a quadrilateral $ABCD$ is a **parallelogram** if each pair of opposite sides are parallel.

11 **Given** $ABCD$ is a quadrilateral with $AB = DC$ and $AB \| DC$.
Prove $AD = BC$ and $ABCD$ is a parallelogram.

12 The quadrilateral $ABCD$ is such that $AB = CD$ and $\angle DAC + \angle ACB = 180°$. Prove that $\angle B = \angle D$.

C8 Prime factorisation *B* NC

This section uses the apparently practical task of arranging unit squares to make rectangles to highlight some important factorisation properties of integers.

Problem 0

> **0** How many different rectangles can be made using exactly 12 unit squares each time?

1 *Four* unit squares (1 × 1) can be arranged to form a *rectangle* (no holes!) in two ways: a single row (a 4 × 1 rectangle) or a 2 × 2 square (a *square* is a special *rectangle*).
Complete the following table. *Make sure your entries are accurate.*

Number of unit squares *n*	Number of different rectangles	Number of squares
3	.	.
4	2	1
5		
6		
7		
8		
9		
10		
11		
12		
14		
16		
17		
20		
24		
27		
32		
36		
47		
48		
49		
72		
81		
83		
91		
97		

2 a List all integers, n, in the table in problem **1** for which *only 1* rectangle can be made.

b The integers in your list all have something important in common. What do we call integers, n, with this property?

3 a List all integers, n, in the table in problem **1** for which *only 2* rectangles can be made.

b These integers, n, all share the property that 'n unit squares can make just 2 differently sized rectangles'. But the integers are not all alike.

Can you identify *two* distinct groups of integers in the list you made in part **a**? (One of these groups contains two slightly different kinds of integers.)

Explain what it is about the integer n that decides which group it belongs to.

c For which of the integers, 121, 123, 125, can only two rectangles be made? Which of these integers belongs to which group?

4 a Now make a third list of those integers, n, in your table for which exactly 3 rectangles can be made.

b You should have included both 12 and 16. But they are in fact slightly different. Can you see why?

How many distinct groups can you identify in your third list?

The problems in this section provide a second glimpse into the world of *prime factorisation*. (In Section T13 *Prime factorisation A* we have already seen how the prime factorisation of an integer allows one to count how many factors an integer has.) In this section each rectangle corresponds to a way of factorising the given integer, n, as a product of two factors.

If we ignore the (very special) integer 1, then positive integers which give rise to just one rectangle (that is, which can be factorised in just one way) are precisely the **i*e *u**e**.

If we then consider integers n giving rise to just *two* rectangles (that is, which can be factorised in *two* different ways), we find that there is more than one way this can happen. The different types depend on what n looks like when it is written as a product of powers of primes. We revisit these differences in Section E8 *More prime factorisation*.

C9 Fractions and decimals NC

0.3, 0.37 and 0.375 are *decimals*.

When you write **0.375**, the **3** stands for '$3 \times \frac{1}{10}$'

the 7 stands for '$7 \times \frac{1}{100}$'

the 5 stands for '$5 \times \frac{1}{1000}$'.

$$\therefore \quad 0.375 = 3 \times \frac{1}{10} + 7 \times \frac{1}{100} + 5 \times \frac{1}{1000}$$

$$= \frac{300}{1000} + \frac{70}{1000} + \frac{5}{1000} = \frac{375}{1000}$$

Any fraction that can be written with a denominator of 10, or 100, or 1000, or 10 000, etc. is called a **decimal fraction**.

$\frac{3}{10}$, $\frac{37}{100}$, and $\frac{375}{1000}$ are obviously decimal fractions.

But what about $\frac{3}{8}$ or $\frac{5}{12}$?

$$\frac{3}{8} = \frac{(3 \times 125)}{(8 \times 125)} = \frac{375}{1000}$$

This calculation shows that $\frac{3}{8}$ can be written as a fraction with denominator 1000, so $\frac{3}{8}$ is a decimal fraction (in disguise).

Problem 0

0 a Write each of these decimals as a decimal fraction (that is, with denominator 10, or 100, or 1000, or ...). Simplify each decimal fraction by writing it in its *simplest form* – that is, so that numerator and denominator have *no common factors*.

  i 0.4 iii 1.25 v 2.0032

  ii 0.12 iv 0.125 vi 0.0625

 b Decide which of these fractions are *decimal fractions*. Write each decimal fraction as a fraction with denominator equal to a power of 10.

  i $\frac{1}{10}$ iv $\frac{1}{60}$ vii $\frac{1}{400}$

  ii $\frac{3}{2}$ v $\frac{5}{12}$ viii $\frac{1}{125}$

  iii $\frac{1}{50}$ vi $\frac{5}{28}$ ix $\frac{1}{375}$

CORE

1 **a** Decide which of these fractions are decimal fractions. Write each decimal fraction with a denominator which is a power of 10.

  i $\dfrac{3}{4}$ **iv** $\dfrac{4}{3}$ **vii** $\dfrac{9}{4}$

  ii $\dfrac{1}{15}$ **v** $\dfrac{3}{20}$ **viii** $\dfrac{3}{7}$

  iii $\dfrac{5}{8}$ **vi** $\dfrac{7}{25}$ **ix** $\dfrac{1}{500}$

  b Write each of these decimals as a decimal fraction (that is, with denominator 10, or 100, or 1000, or . . .). Simplify each decimal fraction by writing it in its simplest form so that numerator and denominator have no common factors.

  i 0.3   **v** 1.25   **ix** 1.096

  ii 0.6   **vi** 2.36   **x** 0.0016

  iii 0.24   **vii** 1.125   **xi** 2.008

  iv 0.35   **viii** 0.875   **xii** 1.3125

2 Write each of these fractions as a decimal.

  a $2 + \dfrac{1}{2 + \frac{1}{2}}$ **c** $1 + \dfrac{1}{1 + \frac{1}{3}}$

  b $3 + \dfrac{1}{3 + \frac{1}{3}}$ **d** $1 + \dfrac{1}{2 + \frac{2}{3}}$

To turn a *decimal* into a *fraction* with denominator 10, or 100, or 1000, etc. is easy, for example

  $$0.3 = \frac{3}{10}; \quad 0.37 = \frac{37}{100}; \quad 0.375 = \frac{375}{1000}$$

However, you may not recognise the resulting fraction as a familiar friend unless you can see how to cancel to express the decimal fraction in its simplest terms – as in

  $$0.375 = \frac{375}{1000} = \frac{3 \times 125}{8 \times 125} = \frac{3}{8}.$$

Now think about working the other way. How can you tell at a glance (without already knowing) whether a *fraction* given in its lowest terms is actually a *decimal fraction* in disguise?

Suppose you *start* with a *fraction* – say $\dfrac{3}{4}$, or $\dfrac{7}{80}$. How can you tell when the given fraction can be re-written as a decimal fraction (and so can be expressed as a finite decimal)? For example, suppose you did not already know that $\dfrac{3}{4} = 0.75$. How could you tell *immediately* that $\dfrac{3}{4}$ can in fact be written as a finite decimal?

CORE

To answer this question in general you need to combine two observations:

◎ a *decimal* fraction is a fraction whose denominator is equal to a *o*e* of 10
$$10 = 2 \times 5, \text{ or } 10^2 = 100 = 2^2 \times 5^2, \text{ or } 10^3 = 1000 = 2^3 \times 5^3, \text{ or } \ldots;$$

◎ so a fraction $\frac{p}{q}$ is a decimal fraction in disguise if it is possible to multiply the denominator to make it equal to 10, or 100, or 1000, or ....

The important thing about $\frac{3}{4}$ is that the denominator, 4 is a *a**o* of $100 = 10^2$.

$$\frac{3}{4} = \frac{(3 \times 25)}{(4 \times 25)} = \frac{75}{100} = 0.75$$

A fraction $\frac{p}{q}$ is a decimal fraction in disguise if the *denominator q* is a factor of $10 = 2 \times 5$, or of $100 = 2^2 \times 5^2$, or of $1000 = 2^3 \times 5^3$, or ....

In other words, the denominator q must have the form

$$2^a \times 5^b.$$

That is, q = (a power of 2) × (a power of 5).

3 Use the above fact to decide quickly which of the following fractions can be written as decimal fractions.

i	$\frac{1}{2}$	vii	$\frac{7}{8}$	xiii	$\frac{13}{14}$
ii	$\frac{2}{3}$	viii	$\frac{8}{9}$	xiv	$\frac{7}{4}$
iii	$\frac{3}{4}$	ix	$\frac{9}{10}$	xv	$\frac{3}{500}$
iv	$\frac{4}{5}$	x	$\frac{10}{11}$	xvi	$\frac{5}{7}$
v	$\frac{5}{6}$	xi	$\frac{11}{12}$	xvii	$\frac{1}{200}$
vi	$\frac{6}{7}$	xii	$\frac{12}{13}$	xviii	$\frac{7}{28}$

Note Fractions like $\frac{1}{3}$ or $\frac{2}{7}$ which are not decimal fractions (that is, which cannot be re-written with denominator equal to a power of 10) can still be written as decimals provided we change the meaning of 'decimal' to allow decimals that 'go on for ever', for example

$\frac{1}{3} = 0.3333333333333\ldots\ldots = 0.3\ldots$ with the 3s repeating *for ever*

$\frac{2}{7} = 0.285714285714285714\ldots\ldots = 0.285714$ with the block *285714 repeating for ever.*

C10   Knights and knaves

Logic is based on the simple principle that whenever two statements contradict each other, at least one of them *must be false*.

This is not explicitly taught in school mathematics, but it is used all the time – even in the simplest calculations, constructions and proofs. In this section you have a chance to see how careful use of this basic principle allows you to uncover the truth even when everything seems hopeless.

The problems in this section concern a strange land where each inhabitant belongs to one of two tribes – the *Knights* and the *Knaves*. Knights are honourable, and so *always* tell the truth; Knaves are dishonourable, and *always* lie. There is no way to distinguish the two types – except by what they say. You are a visitor in this curious land, trying to decide at every turn whether or not you are being told the truth.

Problem 0

> **0 a** On arriving in this strange country of Knights and Knaves the first person you meet is a single man, *A*. You want to ask your way, but are not sure whether you will be told the truth. So you blurt out 'Which are you, a Knight or a Knave?'
> *A* replies 'I'm a Knight.'
> Are you any the wiser?
>
> **b** Further on you meet two inhabitants, *B* and *C*. You decide you had better ask a different question this time, so you try
> 'How many of you are Knights?'
> *B* replies 'One of us is a Knight.'
> *C* immediately responds 'That's not true.'
> Is this enough for you to work out what *B* and *C* are?

Sometimes you can spot something useful straight away: for example, in problem **0b**, *B* and *C* cannot both be telling the truth! So if you could see why they cannot both be lying, you would immediately know that they come from different tribes. In problem **0b** this step is relatively easy.

Suppose both *B* and *C* are lying.

∴ *C* is lying.

∴ *B* is telling the truth – so *B* and *C* are *not* both lying.

However, you often have no choice but to focus on one of the speakers (say *C*) and to examine each of the two possibilities in turn:

 i What follows logically if *C* is lying? (Then *B* is ....)

 ii What follows logically if *C* is telling the truth? (Then *B* is ..., etc.)

1 You meet two other locals, *D* and *E*.
 E says 'At least one of us is a Knave.'
 Could this be a lie? So who belongs to which tribe?

2 You then meet another trio, *F*, *G* and *H*.
 F says 'All three of us are Knights.'
 G says 'Exactly two of us are Knights.'
 And *H* says 'Only one of us is a Knight.'
 Can you decide what tribes *F* and *G* come from?

3 You meet three locals, *J*, *K* and *L*.
 J says 'All of us are Knaves.'
 K says 'Exactly one of us is a Knight.'
 L says nothing.
 Can you work out who belongs to which tribe?

4 You then meet two other locals, *M* and *N*.
 M says 'I am a Knave, but he isn't.'
 N says nothing.
 Is this enough to identify both of them?

5 a You approach a group of three locals, *P*, *Q* and *R*.
  You ask *P* 'Are you a Knight or a Knave?'
  P replies indistinctly, so you ask *Q* 'What did *P* say?'
  Q replies clearly '*P* said that he is a Knave' – at which point *R*
  bursts out 'Don't believe *Q*; he's lying.'
  Can you work out what tribes *Q* and *R* belong to?

 b Next time you approach a group of three locals, *S*, *T* and *U* you
  try a different question.
  You ask *S* 'How many of you are Knights?'
  Again the answer is indistinct, so you ask *T* 'What did *S* say?'
  T replies '*S* said that just one of us is a Knight' – at which point
  U bursts in with 'Don't believe *T* he is lying.'
  Can you work out who is what this time?

6 Another group of five, *V*, *W*, *X*, *Y* and *Z*, comment as follows.
 V says '*W* is a Knight.'
 X says '*Y* is a Knave.'
 Z says '*V* is not a Knave.'
 W says '*X* is not a Knight'.
 Y says '*V* and *Z* are from different tribes'.
 How many Knaves are there and how many Knights?

7 Your attempts to decide who is what sometimes cause offence and you get yourself arrested by two friendly policemen called Tweedledum and Tweedledee. They tell you that you could regain your freedom only if you can work out whether they are Knights or Knaves. To help you Tweedledum says 'We come from different tribes.' But Tweedledee immediately says 'Oh no we don't!' Can you earn your freedom?

8 Having satisfied Tweedledum and Tweedledee, you come across five young men who have just completed a race.

    α (Alpha) 'γ came ahead of me.'

    β (Beta) 'I was 2nd or 3rd.'

    γ (Gamma) 'δ came ahead of ε.'

    δ (Delta) 'I was 4th or 5th.'

    ε (Epsilon) 'α finished ahead of β.'

  a Can you work out how they finished – assuming that all five were Knights.

  b Can you work out how they finished if all five were Knaves?

9 In a neighbouring country there are thee tribes:
Knights (who always tell the truth),
Knaves (who always lie), and
Normals (who sometimes tell the truth and sometimes lie).

  a On your arrival you are met by a group of three, π (Pi), θ (Theta), ρ (Rho), including one member of each tribe.

    π says 'I am Normal.'

    θ says 'That is true.'

    ρ says 'I am not Normal.'

    Work out who is what.

  b Later you meet two people σ (Sigma) and τ (Tau).
σ says 'τ is a Knight.', but τ says 'σ is not a Knight.'
Prove that at least one of them is telling the truth,
but is not a Knight.

C11 Calculating angles *B*

C2

Given any two line segments *AB* and *AC*

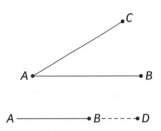

i ∠*CAB* is the angle formed by these two segments at the point *A*

ii if *D* lies on the line obtained when *AB* is extended *beyond the point B*, we say that '*D* lies on AB *produced*' (or '*AB* is *produced* to *D*')

You know

◎ the total angle in a complete turn is 360°.
∴ the complete angle round a point is 360°.
∴ the angle at a point on a straight line (a *straight* angle) is ___°
and a *right* angle (*half* of a straight angle) is equal to ___°

◎ the sum of the three angles in a triangle is equal to a straight angle, that is, ___°.

◎ if two parallel lines are crossed by a third line, then *alternate* angles are equal.

Problem 0

0 In the hexagon *ABCDEF* five angles are as given in the figure.
AB∥*FC* and *AE*∥*BD*.

Calculate the sizes of the angles marked *r, s, t, u, v, w, x, y, z*.

Use the information *given in words in each problem*
i first to draw a sketch diagram
ii then to find the required angles.

1 What angle does the hour hand of a clock turn through

a between 12 o'clock and 2 o'clock?

b between 1 o'clock and 10 o'clock?

c between 10 o'clock and half past 3?

2 What total angle does the minute hand of a clock turn through

    a between 12 o'clock and 2 o'clock?

    b between 1 o'clock and 10 o'clock?

    c between 10 o'clock and half past 3?

3 In $\triangle ABC$, AB is produced to the point D. If $\angle CAB = 51°$ and $\angle ACB = 23°$, calculate the two angles at B. (*Remember to draw a sketch diagram!*)

4 $ABCD$ is a quadrilateral in which $\angle BAD = 105°$, $\angle ABC = 75°$, and $\angle BCD = 63°$. The diagonal BD is drawn and $\angle ABD = 35°$. Find each of the angles at D.

5 The line OK is drawn from the point O to a point K within the angle $\angle MON$. The line OX bisects the angle $\angle NOK$, and the line OY bisects the angle $\angle MOK$. If $\angle MOK = 40°$ and $\angle NOK = 110°$, find $\angle XOY$.

6 In $\triangle RST$ the angle at R is a right angle. The point Z lies on ST such that RZ is perpendicular to ST. If $\angle ZRT = 29°$, find $\angle RTS$ and $\angle TSR$.

7 In $\triangle XYZ$ $\angle XYZ = 36°$ and $\angle XZY = 66°$. The point W lies on the side YZ such that XW bisects the angle $\angle YXZ$. Calculate $\angle XWZ$.

8 In $\triangle ABC$, the side AC is produced to the point D. $\angle CAB = 65°$ and $\angle DCB = 140°$. Find $\angle ABC$.

9 In $\triangle ABC$, $\angle CAB = 75°$ and $\angle CBA = 39°$. The perpendiculars from the vertices A and B onto the opposite sides intersect at the point H. Calculate $\angle AHB$.

10 In $\triangle ABC$, the bisector of $\angle BAC$ cuts the side BC at the point D. Suppose $\angle BAD = x°$ and $\angle ACD = y°$.

    a Find $\angle ADC$ in terms of x and y.

    b Find $\angle ADB$ and $\angle ABC$ in terms of x and y.

11 In $\triangle ABC$, $\angle ABC = x°$ $\angle ACB = y°$. The point D lies on the side BA produced. Find $\angle DAC$ in terms of x and y.

12 In $\triangle ABC$, $\angle ABC = \angle ACB$ and BC is produced to the point D. If $\angle ACD = x°$, find $\angle BAC$ in terms of x.

The result in problem 11 is called the *Exterior angle theorem* 'Each *exterior angle of a triangle is equal to the sum of the two interior opposite angles.*'

C12 Percentage change

Percentages are not numbers; they are *operators*, or *multipliers*, or *scale factors*; you can't have a percentage all on its own – you have to have a percentage 'of' some quantity.

Problem 0

0 a i What is 20% of 40? **ii** What is 20% of 32?

b What is the result if
  i 40 is decreased by 20%? **iii** 32 is increased by 20%?
  ii 40 is increased by 20%? **iv** 48 is decreased by 20%?

c i Trainers are priced at £40 a pair, but I buy them with a 20% wholesale discount. I sell them by adding 20% to my purchase price. At what price do I sell each pair of trainers?

ii Suppose now that I buy trainers at £40 per pair and sell them by adding 20% to my purchase price. Later in a sale I offer a 20% discount to get rid of remaining stock. At what discounted price do I sell each pair of trainers?

Percentage changes cannot be added and subtracted as though they are ordinary numbers; percentages are *multipliers*. 10% of a given amount is equal to $\frac{10}{100}\left(=\frac{1}{10}\right)$ *of that amount*; if we start with a fixed quantity, a 10% increase or decrease changes that quantity by the same amount $\left(\frac{1}{10}$ up or down$\right)$. This does *not* mean that a 10% increase followed by a subsequent 10% decrease cancels out – because the second '10%' is applied to a different total amount!

Problem **0bi** starts with 40 and decreases it by 20%;
problem **0biii** starts with this reduced amount and increases it by 20% – and this does *not* give the answer, 40.

The words 'increase' and 'decrease' encourage thoughts of addition and subtraction. If you remember

◎ that these are *percentage* changes (not *numerical* changes) and

◎ that *percentages* are *multipliers*,

then this approach (using addition and subtraction) can produce the right answer, but it is long-winded, leads to errors, and conceals the simple truth about percentage change. The key to understanding and to reliable calculation involving percentage change lies in *avoiding addition and subtraction*, recognising that percentages are multipliers, and if possible *turning everything into multiplication*.

If an amount is decreased by 20%, the result is ___ % of the original amount.

If I buy a £90 suit in a sale with 20% discount, then I pay 80% of £90,

that is, $\frac{80}{100} \times £90 = £$ ___.

If a meal costs £80 with a 20% service charge, then I pay 120% of £80,

that is, $\frac{120}{100} \times £80 = £$ ___.

In problem **0bi**, 40 is decreased by 20%; the result is $\frac{80}{100} \times 40$.

In problem **0biii** this amount is increased by 20%, so the result is equal to

$$(*) \quad \frac{120}{100} \times \left(\frac{80}{100} \times 40 \right).$$

This should also explain why problem **0biii** and **0biv** give the same answer: compare (*) above with (**) below.

In problem **0bii**, 40 is increased by 20%; the result is $\frac{120}{100} \times 40$.

In problem **0biv** this amount is decreased by 20%, so the result equals

$$(**) \quad \frac{80}{100} \times \left(\frac{120}{100} \times 40 \right).$$

1 Calculate

   a 80% of 40   **b** 120% of 32   **c** 80% of 48   **d** 120% of 40.

2 Yesterday 5% of pupils in my school were absent.
   What percentage were present?

3 A man saves 30% of his take-home pay. What percentage does he spend?

4 What must a number be multiplied by to increase it

   a by 20%?   **c** by 70%?   **e** by 100%?

   b by 17%?   **d** by 83%?   **f** by 139%?

5 What must a number be multiplied by to decrease it

   a by 30%?   **c** by 50%?   **e** by 61%?

   b by 9%?   **d** by 37%?   **f** by 100%?

6 Use a single operation each time

   a to increase 300 by 8%   **c** to decrease 80 by 10%

   b to decrease 400 by 20%   **d** to increase 60 by 30%

7 **a** If quantity A exceeds quantity B by 13%, write the ratio of A to B.

   b If quantity X is 21% less than quantity Y, write the ratio of X to Y.

8 The price of an article is increased by 7%. Write

   a the ratio of the new price to the old price

   b the ratio of the change in price to the new price

   c the factor by which the change in price must be multiplied to give the old price.

9 **a** I bought a second-hand car for £ 4800 and sold it for £ 4000. Find the percentage loss (that is, find the loss as a percentage of the cost price).

    b My daughter bought an old car for £ 1125 and sold it soon afterwards making a 12% loss. How much money did she lose?

10 My favourite restaurant gives me a 10% discount. But to the cost of the meal must be added 17.5% VAT and 12% service charge. If the percentages are to be worked out in turn (with each percentage – whether addition or discount) being based on the previous answer), which order of working leaves me with the least to pay?

11 **a** Yesterday evening my journey home from work took 25% longer than usual. By what percentage was my average speed reduced compared to normal?

    b By what percentage must I increase my average speed in order to reduce by 20% the amount of time a particular journey takes?

12 (Use a calculator for this question.) The percentage change in prices each year is called the *inflation* rate. Sometimes the inflation rate gets worryingly large.

   a Suppose prices increase by 20% each year. How many years would one have to wait before the price of everything was more than double what it is today?

   b Suppose prices were to increase at 50% each year. How many years would one have to wait before prices were more than 5 times what they are today?

   c Suppose prices were to increase at 10% each year. How many years would one have to wait before prices were more than double what they are today?

   d Suppose prices were to increase at 5% each year. How many years would one have to wait before prices were more than double what they are today?

CORE

C13 Approximate calculation: NC Addition and subtraction

Once you have mastered the art of carrying out *exact* addition and subtraction accurately and efficiently you are ready to master the closely related art of *approximate* addition and subtraction.

Pupils are often encouraged to do approximate calculation, or estimation, using poorly understood rules of thumb (e.g. 'Move one number *up* and the other *down* to even things out'). These rules are only appropriate in certain cases and even when they give reasonable estimates, one is left with no idea how the final estimate is related to the exact answer. This section explores approximate calculation in a more mathematical spirit.

Problem 0

0 a i How would you obtain a quick approximate answer to the addition 87 + 32 = ___? Can you tell for sure (without working out the exact answer) whether your approximate answer is too large or too small?

    ii How would you obtain a quick approximate answer to 5674 + 3428 = ___? Can you tell for sure (without working out the exact answer) whether your approximate answer is too large or too small?

b i How would you obtain a quick approximate answer to the subtraction 87 − 32 = ___? Can you tell for sure (without working out the exact answer) whether your approximate answer is too large or too small?

    ii How would you obtain a quick approximate answer to 5674 − 3428 = ___? Can you tell for sure (without working out the exact answer) whether your approximate answer is too large or too small?

1 a i How would you obtain a quick approximate answer to 343 + 176 = ___?

    ii Can you tell for sure (without working out the exact answer) whether your approximate answer is too large or too small?

b i How would you obtain a quick approximate answer to 343 − 176 = ___?

    ii Can you tell for sure (without working out the exact answer) whether your approximate answer is too large or too small?

2 a How would you obtain a quick approximate answer to these?

    i 3055 + 1784   **ii** 4860 + 721

b How would you obtain a quick approximate answer to these?

    i 3055 − 1784   **ii** 4860 − 721

Can you tell for sure in each case (without working out the exact answer) whether your approximate answer is too large or too small?

Approximate *addition* is relatively straightforward. If the two summands in problem **0a** are both made simpler and smaller, then the simplified answer will definitely be **a**e* than the exact answer, for example,

    87 + 32 > 80 + ___ = ___ (*lower* estimate).

If the two given numbers are made simpler and slightly *larger*, then the simplified result will be *a*e* than the exact answer, for example,

    87 + 32 < ___ + ___ = ___ (*upper* estimate).

    ∴. The exact answer lies somewhere between ___ and ___.

3 a Repeat the approximate additions in problem **2a** using the method to find upper and lower estimates for the exact answer by rounding both of the given numbers up or down

    i to the nearest 1000   **ii** to the nearest 100   **iii** to the nearest 10.

b i Suppose you are adding *two* numbers. If you round the given numbers to the nearest 10 (up and down) to work out upper and lower estimates for the exact answer, can you tell in advance how big the gap will be between the upper and lower estimates?

    ii Now suppose you have to add *three* numbers. If you round to the nearest 10 (up and down), what can you say about the gap between the upper and lower estimates?

c i Suppose you are adding *two* numbers. If you round the given numbers to the nearest 100 (up and down) to work out upper and lower estimates for the exact answer, can you tell in advance how big the gap will be between the upper and lower estimates?

    ii Now suppose you have to add *three* numbers. If you round to the nearest 100 (up and down), what can you say about the gap between the upper and lower estimates?

Approximate subtraction is more delicate.

CORE

4 Suppose that in problem **0b** you want a quick *upper* estimate for 87 – 32 and, instead of thinking, you simply *assume* that since it is to be an *upper* estimate you should make *both* given numbers *larger*. Show that you will produce an *upper* estimate that is *smaller than* the exact answer!

To get an *upper* estimate for a subtraction, you have to simplify by making the first number *a**e* and the second number **a**e*!

$$87 - 32 < 90 - 32 < 90 - \underline{\quad} = \underline{\quad}.$$

Similarly, if you want a quick *lower* estimate for 87 – 32, you have to simplify by making the first number **a**e* and the second number *a**e*!

$$87 - 32 > 80 - 32 > 80 - \underline{\quad} = \underline{\quad}.$$

∴ The exact answer lies somewhere between __ and __.

5 a Repeat the approximate subtractions in problem **2b** using the above method to find upper and lower estimates for the exact answer by rounding both of the given numbers up or down:

   i to the nearest 1000

   ii to the nearest 100

   iii to the nearest 10.

 b Suppose you are subtracting one number from another. If you round the given numbers to the nearest 10 (up and down) to work out upper and lower estimates for the exact answer, can you tell in advance how big the gap will be between the upper and lower estimates?

 c When subtracting *two* numbers, if you round the given summands to the nearest 100 (up and down) to find upper and lower estimates for the exact answer, can you tell in advance how big the gap will be between the upper and lower estimates?

6 a Find easy upper and lower estimates for
   7893 – 8436 + 7295 = ___.

 b Find easy upper and lower estimates for
   3863 – 7296 + 4439 = ___.

 c Find easy upper and lower estimates for
   9235 – 3798 – 3864 = ___.

7 I wish to surround a rectangular field with a wire fence. What length of wire fencing should I order if the field is stated to be 407 m long and 273 m wide and each of these measurements is accurate to the nearest metre?

C14 Calculating with measures

Amounts of money, such as £1.32, come ready-made in decimal form (provided you take care with amounts like 'one pound and five pence').

Other measurements may have to be *changed* into decimal form before you can do a calculation efficiently. If the numbers are nice, it can be tempting to avoid changing measurements into decimal form, but as soon as the numbers get more awkward, this is a bad strategy!

In each problem, try to find an efficient way which avoids using a calculator – at least for the early problems. You may need a calculator for later problems, but think carefully about the method you are using.

Problem 0

> **0 a** What would it cost to buy 1 m 32 cm of gold wire at £14 per metre?
>
> **b** What would it cost to buy 1 m 32 cm of gold wire at £13.95 per metre?

1 a What would it cost if a taxi journey of 5 km 230 m was charged at a rate of £2 per km?

b What would the same journey cost if it was charged at £1.84 per km?

2 a What would it cost if a phone call lasting 13 min 24 s was charged at a rate of 5p per minute?

b What would the same phone call cost if it was charged at 4.7p per minute?

3 The total length of three ribbons is 2.6 m. Ribbon A is 60 cm longer than ribbon B. Ribbon C is 50 cm longer than ribbon B. Find the length of ribbon A.

4 a How far will you travel if you drive at 30 mph for 75 minutes?

b What if you drive at 32.4 mph for 75 minutes?

c What if you drive at 47.6 mph for 72 minutes?

5 a A lawn sprayer uses 120 litres per minute.
What volume would it use if it ran for 2 h 20 min?

   b Another lawn sprayer uses 143.6 litres per minute.
How much water would it use if it ran for 3 h 45 min?

6 London and Leeds are 189 miles apart. A car leaves London for
Leeds and drives at 68 mph. At the same time another car leaves
Leeds for London and drives at 58 mph.
How long is it before the two cars pass each other?

7 a What would it cost to carpet a floor 4 m by 3 m if carpet costs
£ 25 per square metre?

   b What would it cost to carpet a floor 4.2 m by 2.8 m if carpet
costs £ 24.80 per square metre?

8 A taxi costs £ 2.20 for the first 1.5 km and £ 0.14 for each
additional 100 m.

   a What would it cost to travel 4 km?

   b If I pay £ 7.66 for a journey, how far did I travel?

9 I walk at 4 km per hour and run at 6 km per hour. I find I can save
3 minutes and 45 seconds by running instead of walking to
school in the mornings.
How far do I live from school?

C15 Drawing conclusions *E*: Angle-Side-Angle congruence

The word 'triangle' always means '*labelled* triangle'. A labelled triangle *ABC* has six parts:

◎ three *sides* (*AB*, *BC*, *CA*), and

◎ three *angles* (the angle $\angle CAB$ at the vertex *A*, the angle $\angle ABC$ at the vertex *B*, and the angle $\angle BCA$ at the vertex *C*).

Section C4 introduced the *SSS congruence criterion* for triangles and raised the question 'Given a triangle *ABC*, which combinations of sides and angles completely determine the *shape* of the triangle?'

Section C7 introduced the *SAS congruence criterion for triangles.*

This section is about the third main congruence criterion – the *ASA congruence criterion*; we show that

ASA: any 'two Angles together with the Side *between* them' are enough to determine the triangle *ABC* completely.

If two angles (say $\angle ABC$, $\angle BAC$) and the side between them (*AB*) in one triangle *ABC* are equal to the corresponding angles ($\angle A'B'C'$, $\angle B'A'C'$) and the side between them (*A'B'*) in a second triangle *A'B'C'*,

then $\triangle ABC$ and $\triangle A'B'C'$ must be equal in all respects, or *congruent*. This is the **ASA** (Angle-Side-Angle) **congruence criterion** for triangles.

Problem 0

> **0 a** Draw (as accurately as you can) a line segment *AB* with *AB* = 10.5 cm. Then use a protractor to construct a line *AX* with $\angle BAX = 108°$ and a line *BY* with $\angle ABY = 36°$. Let the lines *AX* and *BY* cross at the point *C*.
>
> **b** Is the position of *C* uniquely determined by the given segment *AB* and the angles $\angle BAX$ and $\angle ABY$?
>
> **c** Use a ruler to measure *AC*, *BC*. Explain why these measurements are inevitably approximate.
>
> **d** Use the given data about $\angle ABC$ and $\angle BAC$ to calculate the exact size of $\angle ACB$. Hence find the *exact* length of *AC*, and check this against your approximate measurement in part **c**.
>
> **e** How many copies of the (exact) triangle *ABC* are there in a regular pentagon with sides of length 10.5 cm?

> **ASA congruence criterion:**
> Given $\triangle ABC$ and $\triangle A'B'C$ with
> $$\angle ABC = \angle A'B'C',\ AB = A'B',\ \angle BAC = \angle B'A'C'.$$
> Then the two triangles are identical. In particular,
> $$BC = B'C',\ CA = C'A',$$
> and the third angles of the two triangles are equal
> $$\angle BCA = \angle B'C'A'$$
> (which also follows from the fact that the three angles add to ___°).

The ASA congruence condition allows you to *deduce* some of the basic properties of parallelograms and rectangles.

1 **Given** a parallelogram $ABCD$ (a quadrilateral with $AB\|DC$, $AD\|BC$).
Prove that $\triangle ABC$ is congruent to $\triangle CDA$.
Conclude that in any parallelogram, opposite sides are equal and opposite angles are equal.

2 **Given** a rectangle $ABCD$ (that is, a quadrilateral with four right angles).

   a **Prove** $AB\|DC$, $AD\|BC$, so the rectangle is a parallelogram.
     (**Outline proof** Draw BD. Let $\angle ABD = x$. Find $\angle CBD$, $\angle ADB$, $\angle CDB$.)

   b Conclude that $AC = BD$, $AD = BC$.

3 **Given** a parallelogram $ABCD$ (that is, a quadrilateral with $AB\|DC$, $AD\|BC$).
Prove the diagonals AC and BD bisect each other.

The ASA congruence criterion also provides an easy 're-proof' of the fact that 'In $\triangle ABC$, if $\angle ABC = \angle ACB$, then $AC = AB$.'

4 **Given** $\triangle ABC$ with $\angle ABC = \angle ACB$.

Prove $AC = AB$

Proof
Consider the two different (ordered) triangles $\triangle ABC$ and $\triangle ACB$.
    (**A**) $\angle ABC = \angle$ ___ (given)
    (**S**) $BC =$ ___   (same side)
    (**A**) $\angle ACB = \angle$ ___ (given)
$\therefore \triangle ABC$ is congruent to $\triangle ACB$ (by the ___ congruence criterion).   **QED**

5 **Given** $\triangle ABC$ with $AB = AC$. Let the bisector of $\angle ABC$ meet AC at Q, and the bisector of $\angle ACB$ meet AB at P.

Prove $BP = CQ$.

6 **Given** $\triangle ABC$ with M the mid-point of BC.
Let the perpendicular from B to AM (produced if necessary) meet AM at X, and the perpendicular from C to AM meet AM (produced if necessary) at Y.

Prove $BX = CY$.

C16 Ordering fractions

NC

Problem 0

0 a Which is larger: $\frac{3}{8}$ or $\frac{5}{12}$?

b Which is larger: $\frac{137}{57}$ or $\frac{228}{95}$?

To compare any two fractions – such as $\frac{3}{8}$ and $\frac{5}{12}$:

◎ rewrite each fraction in terms of a common unit by multiplying the numerator and the denominator of both fractions to produce an *equivalent* fraction for $\frac{3}{8}$ and an *equivalent* fraction for $\frac{5}{12}$ that have *the same denominator*.

$$\frac{3}{8} = \frac{3 \times 3}{8 \times 3} = \frac{\square}{24} = \underline{\quad} \times \frac{1}{24}$$

$$\frac{5}{12} = \frac{5 \times 2}{12 \times 2} = \frac{\square}{24} = \underline{\quad} \times \frac{1}{24}$$

◎ since '9 lots of $\frac{1}{24}$' is clearly less than '10 lots of $\frac{1}{24}$', we see that

$$\frac{3}{8} < \frac{5}{12}.$$

Once you have chosen the common unit, comparing fractions reduces to comparing the numerators! This makes problem **0b** easier than it looks.

Note In problem **0a**, we did *not* use 8×12 as the common denominator. 8 and 12 have ___ as a common factor, so we used the *least common multiple* of the two denominators $lcm(8, 12) = $ ___ as the common denominator.

This is not logically necessary, but becomes important when the denominators are large $\left(\text{as with } \frac{137}{57} \text{ and } \frac{228}{95}\right)$.

If it is possible to use a smaller common denominator, this simplifies the arithmetic and so reduces the risk of errors. So always look carefully to see whether the denominators have a common factor.

Use the above method to decide, in each case, which fraction is the larger and which is the smaller.

1 Which is larger: $\frac{2}{3}$ or $\frac{3}{4}$?

5 Which is larger: $\frac{3}{8}$ or $\frac{4}{10}$?

2 Which is larger: $\frac{4}{7}$ or $\frac{4}{9}$?

6 Which is larger: $\frac{5}{12}$ or $\frac{11}{25}$?

3 Which is larger: $\frac{2}{3}$ or $\frac{5}{8}$?

7 Which is larger: $\frac{5}{8}$ or $\frac{6}{10}$?

4 Which is larger: $\frac{4}{7}$ or $\frac{5}{9}$?

8 On her five tests this year Laura's marks were $\frac{8}{10}$, $\frac{43}{50}$, $\frac{21}{25}$, $\frac{60}{75}$ and 83 %.
   On which of these tests did she do 'best'?

Decide, in each case, which fraction is the larger and which is the smaller.

9 Which is larger: $\frac{5}{12}$ or $\frac{10}{25}$?

12 Which is larger: $\frac{13}{21}$ or $\frac{21}{34}$?

10 Which is larger: $\frac{5}{8}$ or $\frac{7}{13}$?

13 Which is larger: $\frac{41}{29}$ or $\frac{17}{12}$?

11 Which is larger: $\frac{7}{12}$ or $\frac{6}{11}$?

14 Which is larger: $\left(\frac{8}{5}\right) \div \left(\frac{2}{8}\right)$ or $\left(\frac{5}{2}\right) \div \left(\frac{5}{8}\right)$?

15 Joe and Joanna both like to do well in maths. In the four maths
    tests so far this year, Joe has scored $\frac{46}{51}$, $\frac{23}{24}$, $\frac{24}{25}$, and $\frac{27}{30}$.
    Joanna missed the first test, but scored $\frac{21}{24}$, $\frac{24}{25}$, and $\frac{28}{30}$ on the
    next three.
    Which pupil has the better overall performance?

C17 Word problems *B*

Here is another mixed set of word problems to develop your ability to extract information from words, and then to combine elementary arithmetic and thinking to solve simple problems.

Problem 0

> **0** In conker arithmetic when a '4-er' plays a '5-er' only the winner survives and then becomes an '10-er' (since 10 = 4 + 5 + 1).
> If five '3-ers' play until only one is left, what will the winner have become?

1 A car has five tyres (four on the road wheels and one on the spare wheel). The car travels 30 000 km and all five tyres are used equally. How many kilometres' wear does each tyre receive?

2 Ghulam sells postcards at weekends. He sold $\frac{2}{5}$ of his stock on Sunday and the rest on Saturday. If he sold 25 fewer on Sunday than on Saturday how many did he start with?

3 If 70 % of the children in a class are boys and the number of girls is 16 less than the number of boys, how many pupils are there in the class?

4 Sam, the super snail, is climbing a vertical gravestone 1 metre high, She climbs at the steady speed of 30 cm per hour, but each time the church clock strikes, the shock causes her to slip down 1 cm. The clock only strikes on the hour, so at 1 o'clock Sam slips back 1 cm, at 2 o'clock she slips back 2 cm, and so on.
If she starts to climb just after the clock strikes 3 am, when will she reach the top?

5 Of 400 people at a concert, 55 % are women, 25 % are men and the rest are children.
How many more adults than children are there at the concert?

6 In a club there are 20% more girls than boys. After 50 boys left there were twice as many girls as boys.
   How many girls were there in the club?

7 In a bookshop 31 books are arranged from left to right in order of increasing price. Each book costs £2 more or less than its neighbours. The most expensive book costs the same as the middle book and one of its neighbours together.
   What would it cost to buy the three middle books?

8 When Gulliver awoke in the land of *Lilliput* he found that the people were only six inches tall, compared with his own six feet. Everything else in *Lilliput* was similarly reduced in size (for example, a 'Lilliputian foot' was the same as a human inch).
   How many 'Lilliputian pint' bottles of milk would be needed to provide the human half-pint needed for Gulliver's cornflakes?

9 Moses is twice as old as Methuselah was when Methuselah was one-third as old as Moses will be when Moses is as old as Methuselah is now.
   If the difference in their ages is 666, how old is Methuselah?

10 Five years ago Khalia's father was four times as old as she was. Now he is just three times as old as she is.
   How many years will it be before Khalia's father is just twice as old as Khalia?

 **C18** Area of triangles and parallelograms

> **0** Which of the two shaded rectangles is the larger?

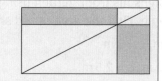

All area calculations can be derived from two basic facts (proved below):

◎ The area of any rectangle is given by the formula
$\qquad$ **A**: area = *base* × *height*.

◎ A diagonal splits a rectangle into two equal right-angled triangles.
$\qquad$ ∴ The area of each right-angled triangle is given by the formula
$\qquad$ **B**: area = $\frac{1}{2}$(base × height).

A: The area of any rectangle is equal to '*base* × *height*'.
This is easy to see if the sides of the rectangle are integer multiples of the basic unit of length.
A 2 × 3 rectangle decomposes into 2 × 3 = 6 unit squares.

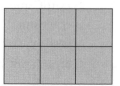

If the side lengths are fractional, choose a *smaller unit* so that the lengths become *integer* multiples of the *new-unit*. Faced with a $\frac{3}{2} \times \frac{5}{2}$ rectangle, the new length unit '$\frac{1}{2}$' fits 3 times into one side and 5 times into the other side.
∴ The rectangle has dimensions 3 by 5 with respect to this new-unit.
∴ The rectangle decomposes into 3 × 5 = 15 'new-unit' squares.

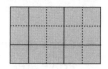

Each 'new-unit' square measures $\frac{1}{2} \times \frac{1}{2}$ in old length units.

∴ 4 'new-unit' squares make 1 'old-unit' square.

∴ The $\frac{3}{2} \times \frac{5}{2}$ rectangle has area $15 \times \frac{1}{4} = \left(\frac{3}{2}\right) \times \left(\frac{5}{2}\right)$ old square units.

1 Find the area of a path running all round a lawn 20 m long and 13 m wide

$\quad$ **a** if the path is 2 m wide

$\quad$ **b** if the path is 2.5 m wide.

2 A rectangular sheet of tin measures 46 cm by 37 cm. A strip 2.5 cm wide is cut off all round the edge. Find the area of the strip cut off.

3 A room 5 m long and 4 m wide has a central rectangular carpet leaving a margin of stained wood 30 cm wide round the edge of the room. Find the stained area.

4 A football fan redesigns his front garden using white paving stones and red shingle. Find the area of red shingle

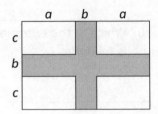

   a if $a = 5$ m, $b = 1$ m, $c = 3$ m

   b if $a = 4.5$ m, $b = 2$ m, $c = 2.5$ m.

B: Each diagonal splits a rectangle into two congruent right-angled triangles, so each has area '$\frac{1}{2}$(base × height)'.
Proof Let *ABCD* be a given rectangle.
We show that $\triangle ABC$ and $\triangle CDA$ are congruent.
$AD\|BC$ and $AB\|DC$ (section C2, problem 5)
∴ (A) $\angle DAC = \angle BCA$ (a∗∗e∗∗a∗e angles)
  (S) $AC = CA$ (same segment)
  (A) $\angle BAC = \angle DCA$ (a∗∗e∗∗a∗e angles)
∴ $\triangle ABC$ and $\triangle CDA$ are congruent (by the ASA congruence criterion)
∴ Each of $\triangle ABC$ and $\triangle CDA$ is exactly ∗a∗∗ of the rectangle *ABCD*.
∴ **area**$(\triangle ABC) = \frac{1}{2} \times$ area$(ABCD)$

$$= \frac{1}{2}(BC \times BA) = \frac{1}{2}(\textbf{base} \times \textbf{height}). \quad \textbf{QED}$$

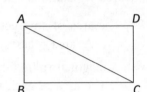

5 **Given** rectangle *ABCD* with *P* a point on the segment *AD*.
Prove area$(\triangle BPC) = \frac{1}{2}(BC \times BA) = \frac{1}{2}$(base × height).

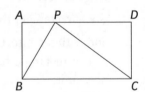

6 **Given** a 1 × 1 square array of dots and points *A, B, C, X, Y, M* as shown.

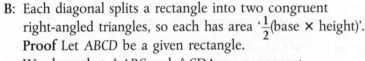

   a Use the SAS congruence criterion to prove that $\triangle BMA$ and $\triangle BMC$ are congruent isosceles triangles.

   b Conclude that $BA = BC$; $\angle BAM = \angle BCM = \underline{\hspace{1cm}}°$, ∴ $\angle ABC = \underline{\hspace{1cm}}°$.

   c Use the SAS congruence criterion to prove $\triangle ABC$, $\triangle CBX$, $\triangle XBY$ and $\triangle YBA$ are all congruent. Then use formula **A** to calculate area$(ACXY) = \underline{\hspace{1cm}}$; ∴ area$(\triangle ABC) = \underline{\hspace{1cm}}$.

   d Finally apply formula **B** to the ∗i∗∗∗ a∗∗∗e∗ triangle $\triangle ABC$ to show that $AB = \sqrt{2}$.

7 **Given** parallelogram *ABCD*.

Let the perpendicular from *A* to *BC* meet *BC* at the point *X*.
Let the perpendicular from *D* to *BC* meet *BC* produced at *Y*.

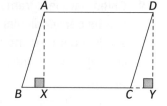

a Use the fact that opposite sides of a parallelogram are equal (Problem **1** in Section **C15** *Drawing conclusions E: ASA congruence*) to prove that $\triangle ABX$ and $\triangle DCY$ are congruent.

b Conclude that $BC = BX + XC = CY + XC = XY$.

c Hence show that area(*ABCD*) = area(*AXYD*) = $XY \times XA$ = $BC \times XA$ = base × height.

The rest of this section proves formula **B** for *general* triangles and proves formula **A** for *general* parallelograms.

Our approach depends on the idea behind problems **1–4**, that is, to interpret each unknown area as the *difference* of known figures. To illustrate this approach we first use **B** to give an elegant solution to problem **0**.

8 **Given** rectangle *ABCD* with vertical *UV* and horizontal *YZ* crossing at *X* on the diagonal *BD*.
Prove area(rectangle *AYXU*) = area(rectangle *CZXV*).
Copy and complete the following proof.
(The trick is to see each region of interest as a *difference* of regions whose areas we already know how to calculate, and then to use the simple idea, if $P = Q$ and $p = q$, then $P - p = Q - q$).

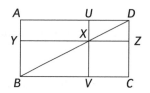

Proof Area($\triangle ABD$) = area($\triangle YBX$) + area(*AYXU*) + area($\triangle UXD$)
and area($\triangle CDB$) = area($\triangle V$___) + area($\square CZ$___) + area($\triangle ZD$___)

But area($\triangle ABD$) = area($\triangle CDB$) (halves of rectangle ___)
∴ area($\triangle YBX$) + area(*AYXU*) + area($\triangle UXD$)
  = area($\triangle VXB$) + area(*CZXV*) + area($\triangle ZDX$)

But area($\triangle YBX$) = area($\triangle$___) (halves of rectangle ___)
and area($\triangle UXD$) = area($\triangle$___) (halves of rectangle___)
∴ area(*AYXU*) = area($\triangle ABD$) − area($\triangle YBX$) − area($\triangle UXD$)
        = area($\triangle CDB$) − area($\triangle VXB$) − area($\triangle ZDX$)
        = area(*CZXV*)   **QED**

Problem 7 proves formula **A** 'area = base × height' for those parallelograms in which the perpendicular from *A* to *BC* meets *BC* *between B and C*.

If in the parallelogram *ABCD* the perpendicular from *A* to *BC* meets *BC* at *B*, then *ABCD* is a *rectangle*, so the formula 'area = base × height' was proved at the start of the section.

If the perpendicular from *A* to *BC* meets *BC* *between B and C*, formula **A** 'area = base × height' was proved in problem 7. Problem **9** takes a slightly different approach to prove formula **A** for a general parallelogram *ABCD*.

9 **Given** parallelogram $ABCD$ with $\angle ABC < 90°$.

Let the perpendicular to the line BC at the point B meet the line DA produced (or extended) at X. Let the perpendicular from the point D to the line BC meet BC produced at Y.

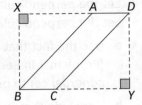

Prove

a   area(rectangle $XBYD$) = $BY \times B$___.

b $\triangle ABX$ and $\triangle CDY$ are congruent.

c   Conclude that $AX = CY$, and so that area($\triangle ABX$) + area($\triangle CDY$) = $CY \times BX$.

Use these results to complete the following:

$$BY \times BX = \text{area}(XBYD)$$
$$= \text{area}(\triangle ABX) + \text{area}(ABCD) + area(\triangle C\text{\_\_\_})$$
$$= \text{area}(ABCD) + [\text{area}(\triangle A\text{\_\_\_}) + \text{area}(\triangle C\text{\_\_\_})]$$
$$= \text{area}(ABCD) + CY \times BX.$$
$$\therefore \text{area}(ABCD) = BY \times BX - CY \times \text{\_\_\_}$$
$$= (BY - CY) \times BX = \text{\_\_\_} \times BX \qquad \textbf{QED}$$

To end we prove formula B: 'area $= \frac{1}{2}$(base $\times$ height)' for a general triangle.

Problem **5** proves formula B 'area $= \frac{1}{2}$(base $\times$ height)' for those triangles in which the perpendicular from P to BC meets BC *between* B and C.

If in $\triangle ABC$ the perpendicular from A to BC meets BC at either B or C, then $\triangle ABC$ has a right angle at B or at C, and the formula B $\frac{1}{2}$(base $\times$ height)' was proved before problem **5**.

If the perpendicular from A to BC meets BC *between* B and C, the formula B: $\frac{1}{2}$(base $\times$ height)' was proved in problem **6**.

So to prove formula **B** for a general triangle $\triangle ABC$ we may assume that the perpendicular from A to BC meets the line BC *outside* the segment BC.

10 **Given** triangle $\triangle ABC$ such that the perpendicular from A to BC (produced) meets the line BC at X *outside* the segment BC. Let the perpendicular to the line BC at the point C meet the line through A parallel to BC at the point Y.

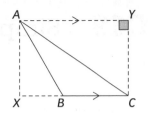

Prove

a   area(rectangle $AXCY$) = $XC \times X$ ___.

b   area($\triangle AXB$) = $\frac{1}{2}(XB \times X$ ___) and area($\triangle YCA$) = $\frac{1}{2}(YA \times Y$___).

c $\therefore$ area($\triangle ABC$) = area($AXCY$) − area($\triangle AXB$) − area($\triangle CYA$)

$$= XC \times XA - \frac{1}{2}(\underline{\quad} \times XA) - \frac{1}{2}(\underline{\quad} \times YC)$$

$$= \left[XC - \frac{1}{2}(\underline{\quad}) - \frac{1}{2}(\underline{\quad}) \right] \times XA \text{ (since } YC = XA)$$

$$= \left[(XC - \frac{1}{2}(XC)) - \frac{1}{2}(XB) \right] \times XA \text{ (since } XC = YA)$$

$$= \left[\frac{1}{2}(XC) - \frac{1}{2}(XB) \right] \times XA$$

$$= \frac{1}{2}(BC \times XA) \quad \textbf{QED}$$

11 a   The rectangle $ABCD$ is cut into two pieces by the segment AP, where P lies on BC.
Given that area($\triangle ABP$) : area($APCD$) = 2 : 5, find the ratio $BP : PC$.

   b   The rectangle $ABCD$ is cut into two pieces by the segment AP, where P lies on BC.
Given that area($\triangle ABP$) : area($APCD$) = 3 : 7, find the ratio $BP : PC$.

 **C19** Simplifying fractions B **NC**

 T21

Problem 0

> **0** Express each fraction in its simplest form and then find the sum.
>
> **a** $\dfrac{7}{42} + \dfrac{9}{108} = \dfrac{\square}{\square} + \dfrac{\square}{\square} =$
>
> **b** $\dfrac{7}{42} - \dfrac{252}{1728} = \dfrac{\square}{\square} - \dfrac{\square}{\square} =$

◎ If you divide a *unit* into 2 equal parts, each part is equal to $\frac{1}{2}$.

$$\therefore 1 = 2 \times \frac{1}{2}$$

If you divide a *unit* into 4 equal parts, each part is equal to $\frac{1}{4}$.

$$\therefore 1 = 4 \times \frac{1}{4} = 2 \times \left(2 \times \frac{1}{4}\right) = 2 \times \frac{2}{4}$$

$$\therefore 2 \times \frac{1}{2} = 1 = 2 \times \frac{2}{4}$$

$$\therefore \frac{1}{2} = \frac{2}{4}, \text{ so } \frac{2}{4} \text{ can be simplified.}$$

◎ $\frac{6}{4}$ can be simplified.

$$\frac{6}{4} = 6 \times \frac{1}{4} = 3 \times \left(2 \times \frac{1}{4}\right) = 3 \times \frac{2}{4}$$

$$\therefore \frac{6}{4} = 3 \times \frac{1}{2} = \frac{3}{2}$$

$$\frac{6}{4} = \frac{2 \times 3}{2 \times 2} = \frac{3}{2}$$

◎ Similarly $\frac{4}{12}$ can be simplified.

$$\frac{4}{12} = 4 \times \frac{1}{12}$$

$$\therefore 3 \times \frac{4}{12} = 3 \times \left(4 \times \frac{1}{12}\right) = 12 \times \frac{1}{12} = 1$$

$$\therefore \frac{4}{12} = \frac{1}{3}$$

$$\frac{4}{12} = \frac{4 \times 1}{4 \times 3} = \frac{1}{3}$$

 118

1 Express each of these fractions *in its simplest form*.

a $\dfrac{2}{4}$ c $\dfrac{7}{42}$ e $\dfrac{9}{108}$ g $\dfrac{48}{60}$

b $\dfrac{4}{16}$ d $\dfrac{8}{80}$ f $\dfrac{13}{52}$ h $\dfrac{60}{156}$

2 Use the simplifications in problem 1 to find each answer in its simplest form.

a $\dfrac{4}{16} - \dfrac{13}{52} = \dfrac{\square}{\square} - \dfrac{\square}{\square} =$ d $\dfrac{48}{60} - \dfrac{8}{80} = \dfrac{\square}{\square} - \dfrac{\square}{\square} =$

b $\dfrac{4}{16} + \dfrac{9}{108} = \dfrac{\square}{\square} + \dfrac{\square}{\square} =$ e $\dfrac{4}{16} - \dfrac{2}{4} + \dfrac{13}{52} = \dfrac{\square}{\square} - \dfrac{\square}{\square} + \dfrac{\square}{\square} =$

c $\dfrac{7}{42} + \dfrac{9}{108} = \dfrac{\square}{\square} + \dfrac{\square}{\square} =$

3 Express each of these fractions *in its simplest form*.

a $\dfrac{45}{162}$ c $\dfrac{105}{147}$ e $\dfrac{252}{1728}$ g $\dfrac{665}{1190}$

b $\dfrac{99}{264}$ d $\dfrac{345}{405}$ f $\dfrac{648}{672}$ h $\dfrac{253}{460}$

4 Use the simplifications in problems 1 and 3 to find each answer in its simplest form.

a $\dfrac{99}{264} - \dfrac{4}{16} = \dfrac{\square}{\square} - \dfrac{\square}{\square} =$ d $\dfrac{7}{42} - \dfrac{252}{1728} = \dfrac{\square}{\square} - \dfrac{\square}{\square} =$

b $\dfrac{45}{162} - \dfrac{7}{42} = \dfrac{\square}{\square} - \dfrac{\square}{\square} =$ e $\dfrac{648}{672} - \dfrac{105}{147} = \dfrac{\square}{\square} - \dfrac{\square}{\square} =$

c $\dfrac{253}{460} - \dfrac{8}{80} = \dfrac{\square}{\square} - \dfrac{\square}{\square} =$

5 Work out each addition and subtraction, giving each answer in fully simplified form.

a $\dfrac{1}{4} - \dfrac{3}{16} = \dfrac{\square}{\square} - \dfrac{\square}{\square} =$ g $\dfrac{1}{48} + \dfrac{1}{60} = \dfrac{\square}{\square} + \dfrac{\square}{\square} =$

b $\dfrac{4}{7} + \dfrac{11}{42} = \dfrac{\square}{\square} + \dfrac{\square}{\square} =$ h $\dfrac{1}{48} - \dfrac{1}{60} = \dfrac{\square}{\square} - \dfrac{\square}{\square} =$

c $\dfrac{2}{7} - \dfrac{5}{42} = \dfrac{\square}{\square} - \dfrac{\square}{\square} =$ i $\dfrac{1}{60} + \dfrac{1}{36} = \dfrac{\square}{\square} + \dfrac{\square}{\square} =$

d $\dfrac{1}{9} - \dfrac{3}{108} = \dfrac{\square}{\square} - \dfrac{\square}{\square} =$ j $\dfrac{13}{60} - \dfrac{7}{36} = \dfrac{\square}{\square} - \dfrac{\square}{\square} =$

e $\dfrac{2}{13} + \dfrac{5}{52} = \dfrac{\square}{\square} + \dfrac{\square}{\square} =$ k $\dfrac{11}{147} - \dfrac{2}{245} = \dfrac{\square}{\square} - \dfrac{\square}{\square} =$

f $\dfrac{5}{13} - \dfrac{7}{52} = \dfrac{\square}{\square} - \dfrac{\square}{\square} =$

 Ratio

One of the difficulties with *ratio* is that ratios come in different forms. The simplest setting is where a ratio expresses the numerical relationship between a *part* of some quantity and the *whole* quantity.

This 'part-to-whole' relationship can be expressed as a fraction and as a ratio:

> 50 p is one *a** of £1 (ratio 1 : 2)
>
> 250 cm is a *ua**e* of 1 m (ratio 1 : 4).

Sometimes ratios are used to express the numerical relationship *between two parts* that make up a 'whole'.

Example 'The number of boys and girls in my class are in the ratio 2 : 3.' When a ratio is given in this 'part-to-part' form, it is mathematically advisable to translate it into the clearer, fractional 'part-to-whole' form: if 'boys to girls' = 2 : 3, then boys form $\frac{2}{5}$ of the pupils in the class, so the ratio between boys and *all children* in my class is 2 : 5.

Problem 0

> **0 a i** Express $4\frac{2}{3}$ as a fraction of $5\frac{3}{5}$.
>
> **ii** Write this 'part-to-whole' as a ratio.
>
> **b i** Express 60 p as a fraction of £8.
>
> **ii** Write this 'part-to-whole' as a ratio.
>
> **c** Divide £35 into two parts so that one part is half as much again as the other. Express the relationship between the smaller and larger part as a 'part-to-part' ratio.

In addition, ratios are used to *compare* unrelated 'wholes': for example, the pay rates for two different jobs may be in the ratio 6 : 5.

To interpret such a ratio one needs to give names to the different quantities: if *x* denotes the rate of pay (say in £ per hour) for the first job and *y* denotes the rate of pay for the second job, then $\frac{x}{y} = \frac{6}{5}$.

'Part-to-whole' ratios

The basic technique underlying all ratio calculations is to express a 'part' as a fraction of a 'whole'. The *part* and the *whole* must be entities *of the same kind*, for example, both might be pure numbers, or quantities with the same units, or even geometrical entities such as line segments.

If, as in problem 0a, the *part* or the *whole* involve fractions, you should

◎ change mixed fractions to simple fractions:

$$4\frac{2}{3} = \frac{14}{3}, \quad 5\frac{3}{5} = \frac{28}{5}$$

◎ rewrite the part and the whole with the same denominator – leaving the numerators in factorised form: do *not* evaluate 14×5 and 28×3

$$\frac{14}{3} = \frac{14 \times 5}{3 \times 5} = (14 \times 5) \times \frac{1}{15}, \quad \frac{28}{5} = \frac{28 \times 3}{5 \times 3} = (28 \times 3) \times \frac{1}{15}$$

◎ ∴ required fraction $= \dfrac{14 \times 5}{28 \times 3}$

$$= \frac{1 \times 5}{2 \times 3} = \frac{\Box}{\Box}.$$

1 Express the first number, or quantity, in each pair as a fraction of the second.

a i $3\frac{3}{4}, 12\frac{1}{2}$ iii $2\frac{2}{15}, 4\frac{4}{5}$ v $3\frac{17}{20}, 12\frac{3}{8}$

   ii $7\frac{1}{3}, 8\frac{1}{4}$ iv $8\frac{1}{6}, 19\frac{1}{4}$

b i   40 p, £ 1   iv   42 p, 28 p   vii   98 p , £ 3.78

   ii   16 p, £ 1   v   £ 1.05, 75 p   viii   £ 2.70 , £ 12.60

   iii   60 p, £ 5   vi   £ 3.24 , £ 5.40   ix   £ 3.40 , £ 1.40

c i   24 cm, 1 m   iv $1\frac{1}{2}$ m, 85 cm

   ii   65 g, $\frac{1}{4}$ kg   v   264 g, 5.94 kg

   iii   450 m, 1 km

2 Use the relevant calculation and answer from problem **1** to just write down the answers.

a Find the number which is $\frac{4}{9}$ of $4\frac{4}{5}$.

b Find the amount which is $\frac{3}{25}$ of £ 5.

c What amount is $\frac{2}{45}$ of 2970?

3 Use the relevant calculation and answer from problem **1** to just write the answers.

a $12\frac{1}{2}$ m of curtain material cost £ 100. What will $3\frac{3}{4}$ m of the same material cost?

b My car travels 66 miles on $8\frac{1}{4}$ litres of petrol. How far can I expect to travel on $7\frac{1}{3}$ litres?

c I have to complete a 33-mile hill trek in one day. If the first 14 miles takes me 8 hours and 10 minutes, how long can I expect the complete trek to take?

d If a kilo of cheese costs £5.40, what weight should one expect to get for £3.24?

e I paid £12.60 for some mangoes. If 3 mangoes cost £2.70, how many mangoes did I buy?

f When jogging I take 1200 strides when running 1 km. How many strides do I take to run 450 m?

4 Percentages are particular examples of 'part-to-whole' ratios: x% corresponds to a 'part- to-whole' ratio of the form '$x : 100$'.

a £280 tax is deducted from a total income of £840. What percentage of income is deducted as tax? Express this in simplest terms as a 'part-to-whole' ratio.

b A school contains 360 girls and 240 boys. What percentage of the pupils are boys? Express this in simplest terms as a 'part-to-whole' ratio.

It often helps to represent the two quantities A, B involved in a ratio using a simple diagram.

$$A \qquad B$$
$$A : B = \underline{\quad}$$

Given two quantities A, B in the ratio $A : B = m : n$.

$$\therefore \frac{A}{B} = \frac{m}{n}$$
$$\therefore A = B \times \frac{m}{n}, \ B = A \times \frac{n}{m}$$

$$A = 3\tfrac{3}{4} \qquad B = 12\tfrac{1}{2}$$
$$A : B = 3 : 10$$
$$A = B \times \frac{3}{10}, \quad B = A \times \frac{10}{3}$$

5 For each pair of quantities A, B find the two multipliers α, β and write the two equations $B = A \times \alpha$, $A = B \times \beta$.

a $7\tfrac{1}{3} : 8\tfrac{1}{4}$ **d** £3.40 : £1.40

b $8\tfrac{1}{6} : 19\tfrac{1}{4}$ **e** $1\tfrac{1}{2}$ m : 85 cm

c £1.05 : 75 p   **f** $2.16\,\text{m}^2 : 3.6\,\text{m}^2$

$$\ldots \times \alpha$$
$$A \longrightarrow B = A \times \alpha$$
$$B : A = \alpha$$

$$\ldots \times \beta$$
$$B \longrightarrow A = B \times \beta$$
$$A : B = \beta$$

'Part-to-part' ratios

To 'divide £ 35 into two parts, *one part half as much again as the other*': the ratio between the smaller part and the larger part is $1:1\frac{1}{2} = 2:\underline{\quad}$.

This 'part-to-part' ratio indicates that, if the 'whole' (£ 35) is divided into $2 + 3$ equal units, 2 of these units will form the smaller part – which is then $\frac{2}{5}$ of the whole.

6 a Divide £ 60
      i in the ratio 2:3   ii in the ratio 5:7   iii in the ratio 4:1.

   b Divide 48 kg
      i in the ratio 3:5   ii in the ratio 1:5   iii in the ratio 9:7.

   c Divide £ 9.60 into three shares in the ratio 5:2:9.

7 In a bag, the ratio of red beads to black beads is 3:4. There are 39 red beads. How many more black beads are there than red beads?

8 Divide £ 66 between three boys X, Y, Z so that X has twice as much as Y and Y has half as much again as Z.

'Comparison' ratios

In a 'comparison' ratio the two quantities being compared may be unrelated, but they must be of the *same kind* (both pure numbers, or both quantities with the same units). So using ratio to compare two separate quantities still depends on calculations like those in problem 1.

9 a I am thinking of two numbers. My two numbers are in the ratio 2:3. The smaller of the two numbers is 6. What is the larger number?

   b I am thinking of two numbers. My two numbers are in the ratio 2:3. The smaller of the two numbers is 5. What is the larger number?

   c I am thinking of two numbers. My two numbers are in the ratio 2:3. The smaller of the two numbers is −9. What is the larger number?

   d I am thinking of two numbers. My two numbers are in the ratio 2:3. If the sum of the two numbers is 50, what are my two numbers?

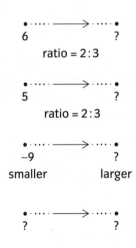

Even if the answer seems obvious, you should never be content just to guess (as you may well have done in problem **8**); rather you should set up and solve equations to make sure you find all solutions – see problem **9**. You must also expect to have to interpret the given information before resorting to purely numerical calculation – as in problems **10** and **11**.

10 I am thinking of two numbers. My two numbers are in the ratio 2 : 3 If the product of my two numbers is 600, what are my two numbers?

11 *X* would take 10 days to lay a brick wall that *Y* can lay in 8 days. *X* and *Y* work together on the job and work at these speeds. If they receive £ 450 between them for the labour, how should the money be split.

12 An employer has two qualified craftsmen and three trainees. The craftsmen are paid for 8 hours a day, the trainees for 6 hours a day. The total weekly wage bill is £ 1012. The hourly rates for craftsmen and trainees are in the ratio 7 : 4. How much does each employee earn each week?

The unitary method

Ratios come into play in any setting where two different kinds of quantity (say weights and prices, or distances and times) are linked, and where they vary in such a way that when one quantity is *doubled* (or halved), the other will also *double* (or halve).

This is exactly how ordinary *prices* work. A price is strictly a rate: *price is the cost per specified unit*. So the total cost is obtained as *price × number of units*.

If the price of cheese is £ 5.40 per kg, $250\,\text{g} = \frac{1}{4} \times 1\,\text{kg}$ will cost $\frac{1}{4} \times £\,5.40 = £\,\underline{\quad}$.

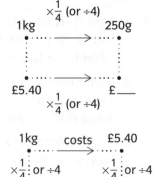

Ratio problems typically provide *three* pieces of information (corresponding to *three corners* of the diagram) and you have to work out a fourth amount: the method is often called the *Rule of Three*.

It is sometimes convenient to modify the way we draw the rectangle to reflect the way a problem is worded – swapping *horizontal* and *vertical*.

If the basic ratio is in the form '1 : ___', or '___ : 1', the calculation to find the fourth amount is relatively easy. If the ratios involved are more awkward, the *unitary method* makes things easier by introducing an intermediate step which has the form either '1 : ___' or '___ : 1'.

Problem 50 nails cost 60 p. What will 80 nails cost?

Solution Given 50 nails cost 60 p

50 and 80 are both multiples of 10

∴ use '10 nails' as our 'new unit'.

$$10 \text{ nails} = 50 \times \frac{1}{5}$$

∴ 10 nails cost $60 \times \frac{1}{5} = $ ___ p

∴ 80 nails = 8×10 nails cost $8 \times 12 \text{ p} = $ ___ p.

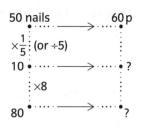

Solve the next six problems by drawing a single rectangle, or a double rectangle, to calculate the required amount.

13 a 50 cm of red ribbon costs 75 p. Find the cost of 40 cm.

b 30 cm of blue ribbon costs 45 p. Find the cost of 20 cm.

14 Two towns 40 km apart are 16 cm apart on a map.

a What distance on the map represents 2 km?

b What is the actual distance between two villages which are 15 cm apart on the map?

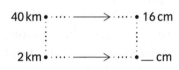

15 A man cycles at 20 km per hour to a station $1\frac{1}{4}$ km away. What fraction of the distance does he cover in the first 3 minutes?

16 I earn £ 4.50 per hour.

a How much do I earn in 4 hours?

b How much do I earn in 75 minutes?

c How much do I earn in t hours?

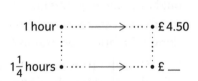

17 My car uses 8 litres of petrol to travel 48 km.

a How far can I expect to travel on 20 litres?

b How far can I expect to travel on x litres?

18 I walk 3 km in 30 minutes.

a How long can I expect to take to walk 5 km?

b What distance should I cover in 75 minutes?

We end with a few mixed problems.

19 After spending $\frac{5}{9}$ of my money I have 72 p left. How much did I start with?

20 **a** $\frac{3}{4}$ of a number is 21. What is $\frac{3}{2}$ of the same number?

  b $\frac{3}{4}$ of a number is −17. What is $\frac{3}{2}$ of the same number?

21 Find x if

  a $12:x = 16:36$ **c** $7.5:20.8 = 3\frac{11}{13}:x$

  b $13:x = 19:9.5$ **d** $x+1:8 = 3.75:7.$

22 $\frac{1}{4}$ of my beads are red, 60 % of the rest are yellow and the remainder are blue. If there are 48 blue beads, how many beads are there altogether?

Ratio and proportion are perhaps the most important topics in elementary mathematics. The simplest applications of arithmetic in everyday life, and the most powerful elementary applications of mathematics to science often depend on ratio and proportion, yet these topics are poorly understood. In the examples section of the Key Stage 3 Framework we read: 'ratio compares part to part; proportion compares part to whole'. This is wrong. It is true that the word 'proportion' is sometimes used in the stated way in colloquial English. For example, one may ask: 'What proportion of the whole class are boys?'. But such a question should be expressed as 'What *fraction* of the whole class are boys?'

A *ratio* compares any two quantities of the same kind: it measures how many times one quantity would go into the other, or which multiplier would turn one quantity into the other. A *proportion* is, roughly speaking, one of our 'rectangular schemas'. That is, a proportion is an equation linking two ratios, for example,

$$50 \text{ nails}:10 \text{ nails} = 60\,\text{p}:12\,\text{p}$$
$$\therefore 10 \text{ nails}:80 \text{ nails} = 12\,\text{p}:96\,\text{p}$$

C21 Highest common factors and least common multiples *B* **NC**

CORE

The *hcf* and the *lcm* of two integers arise most often when working with fractions.

◎ $hcf(12, 18) = 6$, so $\dfrac{12}{18} = \dfrac{6 \times \square}{6 \times \square} = \dfrac{\square}{\square}$

◎ $lcm(18, 12) = 36 = 18 \times 2 = 12 \times 3$, so

$$\frac{5}{18} + \frac{7}{12} = \frac{5 \times 2}{18 \times 2} + \frac{7 \times 3}{12 \times 3} = \frac{(5 \times 2 + 7 \times 3)}{36} = \frac{\square}{\square}$$

*Hcf*s and *lcm*s also arise in tackling certain kinds of word problems.

Problem 0

0 a The material for a large flag measuring 5 m 55 cm by 7 m 40 cm is to be assembled from square pieces of material – all the same size.
If the pieces are to be as large as possible, how many pieces will be needed and what size will they be?

b Rectangular rubber tiles, each 63 cm by 91 cm are to be assembled to make a square playing area in a park. The rectangular tiles must all be oriented the same way (to avoid giving a higgledy-piggledy appearance).
What is the size of the smallest square that can be made in this way?
How many rectangular tiles will be needed?

1 The material for a bedspread measuring 2 m 43 cm by 1 m 89 cm is to be assembled from identical square patches.
If the patches are to be as large as possible, how many patches will be needed and what size will they be?

2 A rectangular plot for a new factory measures 432 m by 276 m. The plot is to be surrounded by a fence, with the fence posts equally spaced round the edge. If the posts are positioned as far apart as possible, how many posts will be needed and what is the distance between them?

3   A rectangular field measuring 486 m by 360 m is to be marked off
    into equal square plots.
    Find the minimum possible number of square plots.

4   A father and son are out for a walk. Each of the father's paces
    is 91 cm long. Each of the son's paces is 63 cm long.
    If they start exactly together, how far will they walk before they
    are next exactly in step?

5   Find the smallest positive integer which leaves a remainder of 3
    when divided into 179 and when divided into 234.

6   Hurdles (fence units, all the same length) are used to fence a field.

    a   Suppose the field measures 396 m by 369 m.
        Assuming that the hurdles fit together perfectly and do not
        overlap, what can you conclude about the maximum possible
        length of each hurdle and the number of hurdles used?

    b   Suppose the field measures 639 m by 396 m.
        What can you conclude about the maximum possible length of
        each hurdle and the number of hurdles used?

7   Two cog wheels are meshed together. Cog A in the first wheel
    starts out meshed with cog B on the second wheel.

    a   If the first cog wheel has 60 cogs and the second has 64 cogs,
        how many times must each wheel turn before cogs A and B
        mesh together again?

    b   If the first cog wheel has 39 cogs and the second has 91 cogs,
        how many times must each wheel turn before cogs A and B
        mesh together again?

8   Four cars go round a racing track at constant speeds, taking
    1 min 17 s, 1 min 24 s, 1 min 38 s, 1 min 52 s respectively.
    If all four cars cross the starting line together, find the time
    that must elapse before they next cross the starting line
    exactly together.

C22 Fractions, division and decimals

Problem 0

0 **a** Write $6 \times (5 \div 9)$ as a fraction in its simplest terms.

    b Write $91 \times (3 \div 14)$ as a fraction in its simplest terms.

    c Write $6 \times (a \div 10)$ as a fraction in its simplest terms.

    d Write $12 \div (9 \div 14)$ as a fraction in its simplest terms.

What you know about basic arithmetic (the four rules) needs to be embedded within the larger tapestry of secondary school algebra. In particular, you need to move freely between fractions, ideas of sharing, and – when necessary – the output from short and long division. When in doubt, go back to the definitions.

Unit fractions

$\frac{1}{2}$ is defined by the equation $\boxed{2 \times \frac{1}{2} = 1}$ (2 halves make a whole).

$\frac{1}{3}$ is defined by the equation $\boxed{3 \times \frac{1}{3} = 1}$ (3 thirds make a whole).

$\frac{1}{3}$ ('1 over 3') is also called the **reciprocal** of 3.

$\frac{1}{q}$ (the *reciprocal* of q) is defined by: $\boxed{q \times \frac{1}{q} = 1}$

$\frac{6}{3}$ is a short way of writing $6 \times \frac{1}{3} \left(= 2 \times \left(3 \times \frac{1}{3} \right) = 2 \right)$;

$\frac{4}{3}$ is a short way of writing $4 \times \frac{1}{3} \left(= 1\frac{1}{3} \right)$;

$\frac{p}{q}$ is a short way of writing $p \times \frac{1}{q}$ – that is, **p** lots of $\frac{1}{q}$.

Sharing/division

$6 \div 3$ is the number of things each person gets when 6 things are shared between **3** people.

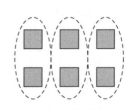

$2 \div 3$ is the amount each person gets when 2 wholes are shared between 3 people.

    Cut each whole into 3 pieces, each equal to $\frac{1}{3}$,

and then give each person 2 pieces: $2 \times \frac{1}{3} = \frac{2}{3}$.

    $\therefore \boxed{2 \div 3 = 2 \times \frac{1}{3} = \frac{2}{3}}$

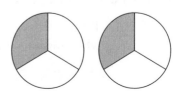

Similarly $p \div q$ is the amount each person gets when p 'wholes' are shared between q people.

Cut each whole into q pieces, each equal to $\frac{1}{q}$,

and give each person p pieces: $p \times \frac{1}{q} = \frac{p}{q}$.

$$\therefore \boxed{p \div q = p \times \frac{1}{q} = \frac{p}{q}}$$

'p divided by q' is the same as 'p multiplied by the *reciprocal* of q'.

All calculations with fractions depend on these definitions. For example

$$\textbf{a} \quad 6 \times (5 \div 9) = 6 \times \left(\frac{5}{9}\right) = 6 \times \left(5 \times \frac{1}{9}\right)$$

$$= 10 \times \left(\underline{} \times \frac{1}{9}\right) = 10 \times \frac{\square}{\square} = \frac{10}{3}$$

$$\textbf{b} \quad 91 \times (3 \div 14) = 91 \times \left(\frac{3}{14}\right) = (13 \times \underline{}) \times \left(3 \times \frac{1}{14}\right)$$

$$= (13 \times \underline{}) \times \left(7 \times \frac{1}{14}\right)$$

$$= (13 \times 3) \times \frac{1}{2} = \frac{39}{2}$$

1 Write each answer as a fraction in its simplest terms.

    a $2 \times (1 \div 4)$ **c** $4 \times (5 \div 6)$

    b $3 \times (1 \div 6)$ **d** $14 \times (30 \div 42)$

Can we calculate $\frac{1}{2} \div 3$ in the same way?

If we imagine *sharing* $\frac{1}{2}$ cake between 3 people, then it is natural to cut

the $\frac{1}{2}$ cake into 3 equal parts and give one part to each person:

$$\therefore \text{each part} = \frac{1}{2} \div 3 = \frac{1}{6}$$

$$= \frac{1}{2} \times \left(\frac{1}{3}\right) = \frac{1}{2} \times (\textbf{reciprocal of } 3)$$

For any value of y, $3 \times (y \div 3) = \underline{}$

$$\therefore (y \div 3) = y \times \left(\frac{1}{3}\right)$$

$$\therefore \text{'}y \text{ divided by 3'} = \text{'}y \text{ times the reciprocal of 3'} \quad (*)$$

That is, the rule for dividing an integer p by an integer q – namely

$$p \div q = p \times \frac{1}{q} = p \times (\text{reciprocal of } q)$$

is also valid when dividing a *fraction* by an integer q.

2 Write each answer as a fraction in its simplest terms.

   a $\frac{1}{2} \div 3$ **c** $\frac{3}{4} \div 3$ **e** $\frac{3}{4} \div 6$ **g** $\frac{4}{9} \div 4$

   b $\frac{1}{2} \div 4$ **d** $\frac{3}{4} \div 4$ **f** $\frac{4}{9} \div 2$ **h** $\frac{4}{9} \div 12$

3 How should you calculate $4 \div (1 \div 2)$?

   a You already know that $1 \div 2 = \frac{\square}{\square}$. Hence $4 \div (1 \div 2) = 4 \div \frac{1}{2}$.

   b You also know that $2 \times \frac{1}{2} = 1$, so the reciprocal of $\frac{1}{2}$ is
     equal to ___.

   c The rule (∗) on page 130 suggests that
     'x divided by $\frac{1}{2}$' = 'x times the reciprocal of $\frac{1}{2}$' = 'x times 2'.

     $\therefore 4 \div (1 \div 2) = 4 \div \frac{1}{2} = 4 \times \underline{\quad} = \underline{\quad}$

4 Use the method of problem 3 to evaluate these.

   a $3 \div (1 \div 2)$ **c** $5 \div (1 \div 4)$

   b $2 \div (1 \div 3)$ **d** $4 \div (1 \div 5)$

Division and decimals

If you need a decimal equivalent for a decimal fraction then Section C9
explains how to proceed: this should suffice for the problems here. (For
practice in the general division process see Sections C28 and C33.)

Fractions	Sharing	Division

Sharing

Share 12 cakes between 3

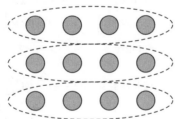

Fractions

$\frac{12}{3} = 12 \times \frac{1}{3}$

$\quad = 4 \times \left(3 \times \frac{1}{3}\right) = 4$

Division

$$3\overline{)1\,2}^{\,4}$$

$12 \div 3 = \frac{12}{3} = 4$

Share 5 cakes between 2

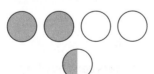

$\frac{5}{2} = 5 \times \frac{1}{2}$

$\quad = \left(4 \times \frac{1}{2}\right) + \frac{1}{2} = 2\frac{1}{2}$

$$2\overline{)5\,.\,0}^{\,2\,.\,5}$$

$5 \div 2 = \frac{5}{2}$

$\quad = 2.5$

Cut one cake in half; then give
two wholes and one half to each
or cut each cake into 2 equal
parts and give five halves
to each person

Fractions	Sharing	Division

Sharing

Share 2 cakes between 5

Cut each cake into 5 equal parts and give 2 pieces to each person

Share 3 cakes between 8

Cut each cake into 8 equal parts and give 3 pieces to each person

Fractions

$\frac{2}{5} = 2 \times \frac{1}{5}$

$\frac{3}{8} = 3 \times \frac{1}{8}$

Division

$$5\overline{)2.0} \quad 0.4$$

$2 \div 5 = \frac{2}{5}$
$= 0.4$

$$8\overline{)3.000} \quad 0.375$$

$3 \div 8 = \frac{3}{8}$
$= 0.375$

5 Write each expression as a fraction in its simplest form, and evaluate it as a decimal.

   a $429 \div 390$ **c** $936 \div 416$

   b $51 \div 136$ **d** $1083 \div 760$

The image of sharing cakes between people may help beginners, but it only makes sense for a *whole number* of people. At secondary level arithmetic has to handle questions like problem **0d**. Questions of this kind arise naturally whenever one is working with ratios.

2 litres of petrol cost £ 3. What will 1 litre cost?

2 litres $\cdots\longrightarrow\cdots$ £3

$\div 2 \vdots \times \frac{1}{2}$ $\therefore \div 2 \vdots \times \frac{1}{2}$

1 litre $\cdots\longrightarrow\cdots$?

12 litres of bottled water cost £$\frac{9}{14}$. How much water will £ 1 buy?

12 litres $\cdots\longrightarrow\cdots$ £$\frac{9}{14}$

$\div \frac{9}{14} \vdots \times \frac{14}{9}$

? litres $\cdots\longrightarrow\cdots$ £1

6 a Write each expression as a fraction in its simplest form.

    i $12 \div (3 \div 4)$ **iii** $36 \div (54 \div 5)$

    ii $12 \div (9 \div 14)$ **iv** $52 \div (91 \div 28)$

  b i If 1 chocolate bar costs 75 p, how many bars can I buy for £ 12?

    ii If 9 pounds of butter cost £ 12, how much will 1 stone of butter cost?

    iii If a truck travels 36 miles on 10.8 litres of diesel, how far will it travel on 1 litre?

    iv If 52 six-inch nails cost £ 3.25, how many will I get for £ 1?

132

C23 Consecutive integers   NC

Two integers that differ by 1 are said to be *consecutive*: 6 and 7 *are* consecutive integers; 6 and 8 are *not* consecutive integers.

Three integers are said to be *consecutive* if the first and second integers differ by 1 *and* the second and third integers differ by 1; 6, 7, 8 *are* three consecutive integers but 6, 7, 9 are *not*.

Problem 0

---

0 a Find three consecutive integers whose sum is divisible by 12.

  b Find another three consecutive integers whose sum is divisible by 12.

  c i Can you find a simple rule which produces lots of triples of consecutive integers whose sum is divisible by 12?

  ii Does your rule produce *all* such triples?

---

1 a Find three consecutive integers whose sum is divisible by 4.
Find another three.

  b Find three consecutive integers whose sum is divisible by 7.
Find another three.

  c Find three consecutive integers whose sum is divisible by 11.
Find another three.

2 a Find three consecutive integers whose sum is divisible by 3.
Find another three.

  b Find three consecutive integers whose sum is divisible by 6.
Find another three.

  c Find three consecutive integers whose sum is divisible by 9.
Find another three.

3 a Find a rule which produces *all* the triples of consecutive integers whose sum is divisible by 3.
Explain why your rule works.

  b Find a rule which produces *all* the triples of consecutive integers whose sum is divisible by 5.
Explain why your rule works.

  c Find a rule which produces *all* the triples of consecutive integers whose sum is divisible by 15.
Explain why your rule works.

4 **a** Find five consecutive integers whose sum is divisible by 4.
   Find another five.

   b Find five consecutive integers whose sum is divisible by 7.
   Find another five.

   c Find five consecutive integers whose sum is divisible by 11.
   Find another five.

5 **a** Find five consecutive integers whose sum is divisible by 5.
   Find another five.

   b Find five consecutive integers whose sum is divisible by 10.
   Find another five.

   c Find five consecutive integers whose sum is divisible by 15.
   Find another five.

6 **a** Find a rule which produces *all* the sets of five consecutive integers whose sum is divisible by 3.
   Explain why your rule works.

   b Find a rule which produces *all* the sets of five consecutive integers whose sum is divisible by 5.
   Explain why your rule works.

   c Find a rule which produces *all* the sets of five consecutive integers whose sum is divisible by 15.
   Explain why your rule works.

Even integers are said to be *consecutive* if they differ by 2: 4 and 6 are two 'consecutive *even* integers'; 4, 6, 8 are three 'consecutive *even* integers'.

7 **a** Find three consecutive *even* integers whose sum is divisible by 4.
   Find three more.

   b Find three consecutive *even* integers whose sum is divisible by 7.
   Find three more.

   c Find three consecutive *even* integers whose sum is divisible by 11.
   Find three more.

8 **a** Find three consecutive *even* integers whose sum is divisible by 3.
   Find three more.

   b Find three consecutive *even* integers whose sum is divisible by 6.
   Find three more.

   c Find three consecutive *even* integers whose sum is divisible by 9.
   Find three more.

9 a Find a rule which produces *all* the triples of consecutive *even* integers whose sum is divisible by 3.
Explain why your rule works.

b Find a rule which produces *all* the triples of consecutive *even* integers whose sum is divisible by 5.
Explain why your rule works.

c Find a rule which produces *all* the triples of consecutive *even* integers whose sum is divisible by 15.
Explain why your rule works.

10 a Find five consecutive *even* integers whose sum is divisible by 4.
Find five more.

b Find five consecutive *even* integers whose sum is divisible by 7.
Find five more.

c Find five consecutive *even* integers whose sum is divisible by 11.
Find five more.

11 a Find five consecutive *even* integers whose sum is divisible by 5.
Find another five.

b Find five consecutive *even* integers whose sum is divisible by 10.
Find another five.

c Find five consecutive *even* integers whose sum is divisible by 15.
Find another five.

12 a Find a rule which produces *all* the sets of five consecutive *even* integers whose sum is divisible by 3.
Explain why your rule works.

b Find a rule which produces *all* the sets of five consecutive *even* integers whose sum is divisible by 5.
Explain why your rule works.

c Find a rule which produces *all* the sets of five consecutive *even* integers whose sum is divisible by 15.
Explain why your rule works.

C24 Fair shares

C21

CORE

In this section you have to share a number of identical circular cakes between a given number of people so that each person is satisfied.

The problems combine the need to work flexibly with fractions with the exercise of visual imagination in two dimensions.

> You are only allowed to make cuts in which each piece of cake is a *sector* of one of the circular cakes, and forms a *fractional part* of that cake.

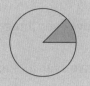

This leads to two quite different types of problem.

a *Fair shares* Here the cakes have to be cut up (into standard fractional sectors) so that each person receives the same amount – but different people may receive their fair share in different ways (for example, one person may receive half a cake in one piece, while another receives two separate quarters).

b *Identical portions* Here the cakes have to be cut up so that everyone receives their fair share *in an identical way*, with everyone receiving identical-looking portions.

Problem 0

> **0** You are given five identical circular cakes.
>
> a Find a way to cut up the cakes into 8 standard circular sectors so that 4 people can be given equal amounts (fair shares).
>
> b Find a second solution.

Fair shares

This section concentrates on the first kind of problem: *fair shares*. To share c cakes between p people so that everyone receives a fair share you could divide each cake in p equal parts – each equal to a $\frac{1}{p}^{\text{th}}$ part of a cake – and then give each person c of these parts:

$$c \div p = c \times \left(\frac{1}{p}\right) = \frac{c}{p}$$

In one sense, this way of sharing the cakes is very efficient, in that it uses just one idea (the same idea every time). In another sense it is very wasteful, in that it uses $c \times p$ pieces. The first group of problems challenge you to create p fair shares using fewer pieces than this.

1 a i Show how to share 2 cakes fairly between 3 people by creating just 4 pieces.

    ii Is it possible to share 2 cakes between 3 people by creating fewer than 4 pieces?

b i Show how to share 2 cakes fairly between 4 people by creating just 4 pieces.

    ii Is it possible to share 2 cakes between 4 people by creating fewer than 4 pieces?

c i Show how to share 2 cakes fairly between 5 people by creating just 6 pieces.

    ii Is it possible to share 2 cakes between 5 people by creating fewer than 6 pieces?

d i Show how to share 2 cakes fairly between 6 people by creating just 6 pieces.

    ii Is it possible to share 2 cakes between 6 people by creating fewer than 6 pieces?

e i Show how to share 2 cakes fairly between 7 people by creating just 8 pieces.

    ii Is it possible to share 2 cakes between 7 people by creating fewer than 8 pieces?

f i Show how to share 2 cakes fairly between 8 people by creating just 8 pieces.

    ii Is it possible to share 2 cakes between 8 people by creating fewer than 8 pieces?

2 a i Show how to share 3 cakes fairly between 2 people by creating just 4 pieces.

    ii Is it possible to share 3 cakes between 2 people by creating fewer than 4 pieces?

b i Show how to share 3 cakes fairly between 4 people by creating just 6 pieces.

    ii Is it possible to share 3 cakes between 4 people by creating fewer than 6 pieces?

3 a You wish to share 3 cakes fairly between 5 people.

    i What is the smallest possible number of pieces needed? Justify your claim.

    ii Show how to share 3 cakes between 5 people using this smallest number of pieces.

b You wish to share 3 cakes fairly between 6 people.

    i What is the smallest possible number of pieces needed? Justify your claim.

    ii Show how to share 3 cakes between 6 people using this smallest number of pieces.

c You wish to share 3 cakes fairly between 7 people.

    i What is the smallest possible number of pieces needed? Justify your claim.

    ii Show how to share 3 cakes between 7 people using this smallest number of pieces.

4 You wish to share 3 cakes fairly between 8 people.

a What is the smallest possible number of pieces needed? Try to justify your claim.

b Show how to share 3 cakes between 8 people using this smallest number of pieces.

5 a Show how to cut 5 cakes into 10 pieces so that 6 people each receive equal amounts.

b Show how to cut 5 cakes into 11 pieces so that 7 people each receive equal amounts.

c Show how to cut 5 cakes into 12 pieces so that 8 people each receive equal amounts.

6 Show how to cut 6 cakes into 12 pieces so that 7 people each receive equal amounts.

7 Show how to cut 7 cakes into 18 pieces so that 12 people can receive equal amounts.

8 Let $c = 2$ (so there are just 2 cakes to be shared).

a Find the minimum possible number N of pieces needed to create *fair shares* for p people.

Number of people, p	1	2	3	4	5	6	7	8	9	10
Minimum number of pieces required, N	2									

b What is the minimum number of pieces needed to create *fair shares* when p is even? Prove your claim.

c What is the minimum number of pieces needed to create *fair shares* when p is odd? Prove your claim.

C25 Generalised arithmetic

NC

T7

In primary school an expression such as

$$12 \times 17 - 3 \times 24 - 6 \times 22$$

is likely to be evaluated term by term. But progress in arithmetic demands that we begin to look for ways of reducing the need for blind calculation — mainly by noticing and exploiting hidden *structure*. For example, $24 = \underline{\quad} \times 12$, so

$$12 \times 17 - 3 \times 24 = 12 \times 17 - \underline{\quad} \times 12 = 12 \times \underline{\quad}.$$
$$\therefore \quad 12 \times 17 - 3 \times 24 - 6 \times 22 = 12 \times 11 - 6 \times 22 = \underline{\quad}.$$

With numbers, it may look like an accident when something that at first seems nasty turns out to be as simple as this. But this kind of 'accident' happens rather often in mathematics, so you need to stay alert.

The most significant development in modern mathematics that allowed ordinary people to see, and to exploit, this simplicity just beneath the surface was the idea (around 1600) of using symbols to stand for unknown numbers, and to calculate with them *as though they were actual numbers*.

The easiest way to simplify in algebra is to *collect terms*. You know that

$$3 \times 20 + 7 \times 20 = (3 + \underline{\quad}) \times 20 = \underline{\quad} \times 20 = \underline{\quad}$$

We also know that the same calculation works if 20 is replaced by any other number. So if we let y stand for an unspecified number, we can write

$$3 \times y + 7 \times y = (3 + 7)y = 10y$$

When doing algebra, we omit the multiplication sign $\times$. This is done partly to avoid confusing the multiplication sign '$\times$' with the letter x, but mainly to simplify what the eye has to grasp. We also drop the division sign $\div$ and write expressions involving division by using fractions instead. This has the advantage of making it easier for the eye (and the mind) to separate the operations of addition and subtraction from those of multiplication and division.

Problem 0

> **0** Simplify each expression without evaluating each term. (Use the rules of arithmetic.)
>
> **a** $12 \times 17 - 3 \times 24 - 6 \times 22 =$
>
> **b** $(4 \times 17 + 3 \times 12) - 2 \times (12 + 17) =$
>
> **c** $(4a + 3b) - 2(b + a) + 1 - b =$
>
> **d** $(20 + 1) \times (20 - 1) = 20 \times (\underline{\quad}) + 1 \times (\underline{\quad}) = 20 \times \underline{\quad} - \underline{\quad} =$
>
> **e** $(a + 1)(a - 1) = (a + 1) \times (a - 1) =$

It may be worth looking more closely at the last two parts of problem **0**. When simplifying algebraic expressions never try to run before you can walk! To multiply out brackets, think clearly and take one step at a time.

When you see '20 − 1', you should realise that '20' is a nice number which you do not want to throw away. If we avoid replacing '20 − 1' by 19, and treat the bracket (20 − 1) as a single entity, then

'20 + 1' lots of (20 − 1) equals '20 lots' plus '1 lot' of (20 − 1)

$\therefore (\mathbf{20 + 1}) \times (20 - 1) = 20 \times (20 - 1) + \mathbf{1} \times (20 - 1)$
$= [20 \times 20 - 20 \times 1] + [1 \times 20 + 1 \times (-1)]$
$= 20^2 - \underline{} = \underline{}$

Similarly

$(a + 1) \times (a - 1) = a(a - 1) + \mathbf{1} \times (a - 1)$
$= [a \times a - a \times 1] + [1 \times a + 1 \times (-1)]$
$= a^2 - \underline{}$

1 Simplify each expression as much as possible.

  a $x + x + y - x + y - x - y$

  b $a - b - 2a + 2b - a - b$

  c $a + 2b - 3(a + b) + 2a + b$

  d $7c - 2d + 3 - 5c - d - 2c$

  e $3x + y + 3 - 3(x + y)$

  f $2(c - x + 1) + 2(x - c)$

  g $5(x + y) - (5x + y)$

  h $3(2c + 1) - (6c + 3)$

2 Evaluate

  a $2(c - x + 1) + 2(x - c)$ when $c = 17$, $x = -32$.

  b $a + 2b - 3(a + b) + 2a + b$ when $a = -\dfrac{13}{3}$, $b = \dfrac{7}{5}$.

  c $7c - 2d + 3 - 5c - d - 2c$ when $c = \dfrac{9}{2}$, $d = -1$.

  d $3x + y + 3 - 3(x + y)$ when $x = 1$, $y = -1$.

3 Simplify each expression as much as possible.

  a $(2a - b) + (2b - c) + (2c - a)$

  b $(3a - 2b) + (2b - c) + (c - a)$

  c $2(a + 1) + a(a - 3) + a$

  d $a + 1 - (a + 1)a$

  e $(x + 3)(x + 2) = x(\_\_\_) + 3(\_\_\_)$

  f $(x - 3)(x - 4) = x(\_\_\_) - 3(\_\_\_)$

  g $(2x + 1)(x - 3) = 2x(\_\_\_) + (\_\_\_)$

  h $(x + 3)^2 = (\_\_\_)(x + 3)$

  i $(x + 1)^2 - x(x + 2)$

  j $a^2 + 1 - (a + 1)^2$

  k $5x(y - 2z) - [5zy - 10xz]$

  l $x(y + 2z) - z.2x - \left(\dfrac{x}{2}\right)2y$

  m $6xy + (x - 2y)(x + 2y) - (3x - 2y)2y$

4 For an x by y by z cuboid, write expressions for the volume, V, the total surface area, A, and the total length, L, of all the edges.

5 The rectangle $OABC$ has O at the origin $(0,0)$ and $B = (x,y)$.
XY is parallel to the x-axis and VZ is parallel to the y-axis.
W lies on the diagonal OB and has coordinates (ax, ay).

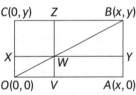

  a Write in simplified form the areas of the rectangles

    i $XWZC$ **ii** $VAYW$ **iii** $OVWX$ **iv** $WYBZ$

  b Which two rectangles in part **a** always have equal area?

6 You are given a cuboid.

  a Suppose the different faces have areas $10\,cm^2$, $30\,cm^2$ and $48\,cm^2$. What is the volume of the cuboid and what are the lengths of the edges?

  b Suppose the different faces have areas $12\frac{1}{2}\,cm^2$, $15\,cm^2$ and $30\,cm^2$. What is the volume of the cuboid and what are the lengths of the edges?

  c Suppose the different faces have areas $\dfrac{4}{15}\,cm^2$, $\dfrac{25}{6}\,cm^2$ and $\dfrac{9}{10}\,cm^2$. What is the volume of the cuboid and what are the lengths of the edges?

C26 Enlargement *B*

Suppose you are given a geometrical figure. If all *horizontal* and *vertical* lengths are *doubled* (say), you might think it is obvious that all other lengths should also double. But this is far from obvious. In this section you have to find some *proof* (you do not need to use P∗∗∗a∗o∗a∗' theorem).

Problem 0

0 a Draw a rectangle *ABCD* with base *AB* = 4 cm and height *AD* = 3 cm. Measure the lengths of the diagonals *AC, BD*.

b Suppose you were to draw a rectangle *WXYZ* with base *WX* = 8 cm and height *WZ* = 6 cm. What should the length of the diagonals *WY, XZ* be? Find some way to *prove* your claim.

---

1 Suppose you were to draw a rectangle *STUV* with base *ST* = 12 cm and height *SV* = 9 cm.
What should the length of the diagonals *SU, TV* be?
Prove your claim.

2 a Copy this octagon onto 1 cm square dotty paper.
Measure the distance *MD* from the mid-point *M* of *AB* to the vertex *D*.
Measure the distances *AC, AD* as accurately as you can.

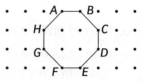

b Draw a '2 × enlargement', *A′B′C′D′E′F′G′H′*, of *ABCDEFGH*.

   i What should the distance *M′D′* be from the mid-point *M′* of the side *A′B′* to *D′*?
Devise a simple proof to show that your claim is correct.

   ii What should the distances *A′C′* and *A′D′* be?
Devise a proof to justify your claim.

c Draw a '3 × enlargement', *A″B″C″D″E″F″G″H″*, of *ABCDEFGH*.

   i What should the distance *M″D″* be from the mid-point *M″* of the side *A″B″* to *D″*?
Give a proof to show that your claim is correct.

   ii What should the distances *A″C″* and *A″D″* be?
Give a proof to justify your claim.

3 a Copy this sloping square $ABCD$ onto 1 cm square dotty paper.

   i Explain why $ABCD$ is a square.

   ii Measure the side AB and the diagonal AC as accurately as you can.

   iii Work out the exact area of the square $ABCD$.

b Draw a $2 \times$ enlargement, $A'B'C'D'$, of $ABCD$.

   i What should the lengths of the side $A'B'$ and the diagonal $A'C'$ be?
   Devise a simple proof to show that your claim is correct.

   ii What should the area of the square $A'B'C'D'$ be?
   Prove your claim.

c Draw a $3 \times$ enlargement, $A''B''C''D''$, of $ABCD$.

   i What should the lengths of the side $A''B''$ and the diagonal $A''C''$ be?
   Give a simple proof to show that your claim is correct.

   ii What should the area of the square $A''B''C''D''$ be?
   Prove your claim.

4 a Draw an isosceles right-angled triangle ABC with $AB = AC = 12$ cm.
   Measure the hypotenuse BC as accurately as you can.

b Suppose you were to draw an isosceles right-angled triangle, $A'B'C'$, with $A'B' = A'C' = 24$ cm. What should the length of the hypotenuse, $B'C'$, be? Prove your claim.

c Suppose you were to draw an isosceles right-angled triangle $A''B''C''$ with $A''B'' = A''C'' = 36$ cm. What should the length of the hypotenuse, $B''C''$, be? Prove your claim.

5 Go back to the rectangle in problem **0a** and the triangle ABC with $AB = 4$ cm, $BC = 3$ cm.

a Construct the perpendicular BL from B to AC as accurately as you can. Measure BL.

b Draw a right-angled triangle, $A'B'C'$, with base $A'B' = 8$ cm and height, $B'C' = 6$ cm. Construct the perpendicular, $B'L'$, from B' to the hypotenuse $A'C'$.
What should the ratio $B'L' : BL$ be? Prove your claim.
Measure $B'L'$ to check.

What counts as a proof? In problem **5b** you must somehow think of triangle $A'B'C'$ as half of a rectangle $A'B'C'D'$ and then link the corresponding rectangle $ABCD$ in problem **5a** and the rectangle $A'B'C'D'$ in problem **5b**. One way to do this is to use the mid-point B'' of $A'B'$ and the mid-point D'' of $A'D'$ to divide $A'B'C'D'$ into four copies of the rectangle $ABCD$. It is then not hard to prove that

◎ the perpendicular $B''L''$ from B'' to $A'C'$ is equal to BL in the rectangle $ABCD$ (since $\triangle A'B''L''$ is congruent to $\triangle ABL$) and

◎ $B''L''$ is exactly half $B'L'$. (Let the line through L''parallel to $A'B'$ meet $B'L'$ at X. Then $B''B'XL''$ is a parallelogram; $\therefore L''B'' = XB'$. And $\triangle L''XL'$ is congruent to $\triangle A'B''L''$; $\therefore L'X' = L''B''$.)

---

6 a Draw a line segment *PR* of length 10 cm. Construct the circle with centre *P* passing through *R* and the circle with centre *R* passing through *P*. Let these two circles meet at *Q* and at *S*.

  i What can you say about triangles *PQR* and *PSR*? Justify your claim.

  ii Let *QS* and *PR* meet at *M*.
    Which congruence criterion implies that *QS* bisects ∠*PQR*? Which congruence criterion then implies that *M* must be the *i*-*oi** of *PR*? What should the ratio *QS* : *QM* be? Measure *QM* and *QS* to check.

b Suppose you were to draw a line segment *P'R'* of length 20 cm, and that you then constructed points *Q'*, *S'*, *M'* exactly as in part **a**.

  i What can you say about the ratios *Q'M'* : *QM* and *Q'S'* : *QS*?

  ii Make a sketch of triangle *P'Q'R'*. Mark the mid-point *M'* of *P'R'*, the mid-point *N'* of *P'Q'* and the mid-point *L'* of *Q'R'*. Use your sketch to prove the claim you made in part **i**.

C27   Cuboids and volumes   NC

Problem 0

> **0** A tank, in the shape of a cuboid with base 40 cm by 30 cm and height 20 cm, is full of water.
> How many litres must have been removed from the tank if the depth of water falls to 16 cm?

1 a How many cubes of edge length 2 cm are needed to make a 6 cm × 8 cm × 10 cm cuboid?

b What is the surface area of the cuboid?

2 How many litres of water can one fit in a 10 cm × 16 cm × 8 cm (cuboid) tank?

3 A tank is 50 cm wide and 60 cm long. It contains 42 litres of water when it is $\frac{1}{3}$ full. Find the height of the tank.

4 A tank 75 cm long and 40 cm wide is completely full. When 24 litres of water are removed it is $\frac{1}{3}$ full. Find the height of the tank.

5 A fish tank 40 cm long and 30 cm wide contains water to a depth of 15 cm and a stone, which is completely submerged. When the stone is removed the water level falls by 6 cm.
Find the volume of the stone.

6 An 8 cm × 10 cm × 12 cm brick is placed on the bottom of an empty 25 cm × 30 cm × 15 cm cistern.
How many litres of water are needed to fill the cistern?

7 A tank 60 cm long, 35 cm wide and 36 cm high contains water to a depth of 14 cm. When a stone is inserted (and completely submerged) the water level rises to $\frac{2}{3}$ the height of the tank.
Find the volume of the stone.

8 A tank 50 cm long and 30 cm wide is $\frac{4}{5}$ full of water. When six cubes
   of edge length 10 cm are placed in the water, the level rises to
   the brim. Find the height of the tank.

9 A tank 30 cm long, 15 cm wide and 20 cm high contains water
   to a depth of 15 cm. Some metal cubes of edge length 5 cm
   are placed on the bottom of the tank raising the water level
   to the brim. How many cubes were inserted?

10 A 40 cm × 30 cm × 15 cm tank is filled from a tap at a rate of
   12 litres per minute. How long does it take to fill the tank?

11 An 80 cm × 50 cm × 60 cm tank is full and water is drained off
   at a rate of 15 litres per minute. How long does it take to empty
   the tank?

12 A tank 40 cm long and 25 cm wide contains three metal cubes
   of edge length 10 cm. It takes $3\frac{1}{2}$ minutes to fill the tank from
   a tap at a rate of 10 litres per minute. Find the height of the tank.

 **C28** Division: Integers **NC**

There are three good reasons for working hard to master the division algorithm.

◎ It develops the mental arithmetic you learned in primary school.

◎ It is one of the simplest examples of the kind of multi-step procedures, or algorithms, which lie at the heart of mathematics.

◎ It is essential if you are later to understand decimals.

Each of these reasons is enough to make division a key goal at age 10–13.

Problem 0

> **0 a** Use short division (and the standard layout) to work out
>   **i** 1001 ÷ 7   **ii** 688 ÷ 43
>
> **b** Use long division (and the standard layout) to work out
>   18 323 ÷ 73.

Do the *short* divisions on this page using the standard layout.
For example, to calculate 688 ÷ 43, write

$$4\,3\,\overline{)6\,8\,8}$$

First divide 43 into 68: 68 = **1** × 43 + *25*,
    that is,   68 tens = (**1** × 43) tens + *25* tens
Say '43 into 68 goes **1** time, with remainder *25*', write

$$\overset{\displaystyle 1}{4\,3\,\overline{)6\,8\;^{25}8}}$$

Next divide 43 into 258: 258 = 43 × **6** remainder 0, write

$$\overset{\displaystyle 1\;\;6}{4\,3\,\overline{)6\,8\;^{25}8}}$$

$$\therefore 688 = 43 \times \underline{16}$$

1 $1\,1\,\overline{)7\,0\,0\,7}$ $\therefore 7007 = 11 \times \underline{\quad}$

2 $1\,3\,\overline{)7\,0\,0\,7}$ $\therefore 7007 = 13 \times \underline{\quad}$

3 $2\,3\,\overline{)7\,0\,1\,5}$

4 $3\,4\,\overline{)7\,0\,0\,4}$

> **5** Work out the missing digits in these divisions.
>
> **a** $1\,2\,\overline{)6\,*\,8}$ with quotient $*\,*$
>
> **b** $*\,2\,\overline{)2\,*\,2}$ with quotient $2\,*$
>
> **c** $3\,*\,\overline{)*\,*\,*}$ with quotient $3\,*$

6 Use careful reasoning to find *all possible* ways of completing these short divisions.

a
```
      * 5
   * )7 *
```
b
```
         * *
   9 * )* * * *
```

The *long* divisions on this page should be done using the standard layout.

For example, to calculate $18\,323 \div 73$, write
```
   7 3 )1 8 3 2 3
```

First divide 73 into '183': $2 \times 73 = 146$, so
   73 goes **2** times with remainder $183 - 146 = 37$.

Next divide 73 into '372': $5 \times 73 = 365$, so
   73 goes **5** times with remainder $372 - 365 = 7$.

Finally 73 into 73 goes **1** time.
   $\therefore 18\,323 \div 73 = \mathbf{251}$

```
                2 5 1
   7 3 )1 8 3 2 3
         1 4 6
         ─────
           3 7 2
           3 6 5
           ─────
               7 3
```

7 Fill in the missing digits in the long division on the right.

```
               * * *
   2 1 )4 6 8 3
         4 *
         ───
           * 8
           * *
           ───
             * *
             * *
             ───
```

8
```
   2 3 )3 7 0 3
         * *
         ───
         * * *
         * * *
         ─────
             * *
             * *
             ───
```

9
```
   4 6 )1 4 7 8 4 4
           * * *
           ─────
             * *
             * *
             ───
               * *
               * *
               ───
                 * * *
                 * * *
                 ─────
```

10
```
   2 3 7 )7 0 8 6 3
           * * *
           * * * *
           * * * *
           ───────
             * * * *
             * * * *
             ───────
```

11 Work out the missing digits in the division on the right.

```
                 4 * *
   * * )* * 7 *
         * *
         ───
         * * 7
         * * *
         ─────
             * *
             * *
             ───
```

C29 Prime factorisation *C*

NC

Problem 0

> **0** Factorise 72 by dividing successively by obvious prime factors.

72 is clearly divisible by the *prime number* 2, so we divide by 2.
The result − 36 − is again divisible by the *prime* number 2.
Continuing the division process …

$$\ldots \text{ we find: } \underline{72} = 2 \times 36$$
$$= 2 \times 2 \times 18$$
$$= 2 \times 2 \times 2 \times 9 = 2^3 \times 3^2$$

Use this method to factorise each of the integers below as a product
of prime powers, picking an obvious *prime factor* to divide by at
each stage.

1 216 $)\underline{216}$

∴ 216 = ___ × ___

4 147 $)\underline{147}$

∴ 147 =

2 600 $)\underline{600}$

∴ 600 =

5 686 $)\underline{686}$

∴ 686 =

3 720 $)\underline{720}$

∴ 720 =

6 162 $)\underline{162}$

∴ 162 =

> **7** Use the prime factorisations of 216, 600, 720, 147, 686 and 162 to
> decide quickly which of these integers is a multiple
>
> **a** of 6   **b** of 7   **c** of 8   **d** of 9

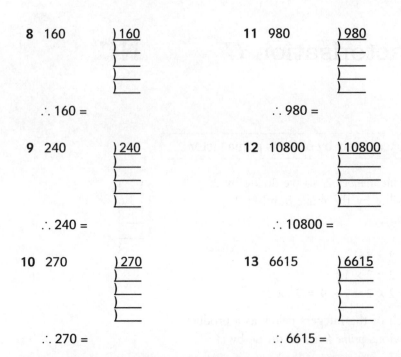

8 160   )160

∴ 160 =

9 240   )240

∴ 240 =

10 270   )270

∴ 270 =

11 980   )980

∴ 980 =

12 10800   )10800

∴ 10800 =

13 6615   )6615

∴ 6615 =

14 During the 1914–18 War, in the Po Valley in Italy, a skeleton, a battered uniform and a halberd (a weapon no longer than 10 feet) were found. Archaeologists discovered that they belonged to a French captain. The length, in feet, of the halberd (a whole number) times the number of days in the month in which the French captain was killed times half the number of years between the death of the captain and the discovery of his skeleton times half the age of the captain when he died makes 451 066.

At which battle was the captain killed?

A Torino, February 1522   **D** Marengo, June 1800

B Cremona, March 1712   **E** Castiglione, August 1796

C Pavia, February 1512

CORE

We first meet fractions, such as $\frac{2}{3}$, as 'operators': that is, as a description of an action. For example,

◎ Find '$\frac{2}{3}$ of something'. The 'something' is taken as our *unit*, and is divided into 3 equal parts, then 2 of these parts are taken.

◎ 'Share 2 equal units fairly between 3 people.' The 2 equal units must be divided into 3 equal portions; then 1 part is taken.

Later we extract from these initial images the important idea that a fraction is actually *a number in its own right*. We then need to learn to think and to calculate with these new numbers. For example,

'$\frac{1}{3}$ of some unit' is greater than '$\frac{1}{4}$ of the same unit'

and is less than '$\frac{1}{2}$ of the same unit'

$$\therefore \frac{2}{3} = 2 \times \frac{1}{3} \text{ is } greater \text{ than } 2 \times \frac{1}{4} = \frac{1}{2}$$

and is *less than* $2 \times \frac{1}{2} = 1$.

We have to learn to work with $\frac{2}{3}$ as it stands, and to resist the feeling that it needs to be evaluated (for example, as $\frac{2}{3} = 2 \div 3 = \underline{\quad}$).

Problem 0

> **0 a** $\frac{1}{2} \times \frac{2}{3} =$ **b** $\frac{1}{2} \times \frac{2}{3} \times \frac{3}{4} =$

The simple cancellation rules that make these calculations easy must be clearly understood before proceeding.

a $\qquad \frac{2}{3} = 2 \times \frac{1}{3}$

$\therefore \frac{1}{2} \times \frac{2}{3} = \frac{1}{2} \times \left(2 \times \frac{1}{3}\right) = \dfrac{\square}{\square}$ (since '$\frac{1}{2}$ of 2 units' is 1 unit)

b $\qquad \frac{3}{4} = 3 \times \frac{1}{4}$

$\therefore \frac{2}{3} \times \frac{3}{4} = \frac{2}{3} \times \left(3 \times \frac{1}{4}\right) = \dfrac{\square}{\square}$ (since '$\frac{2}{3}$ of 3 units' is 2 units)

$\therefore \frac{1}{2} \times \frac{2}{3} \times \frac{3}{4} = \frac{1}{2} \times \frac{2}{4} \quad = \dfrac{\square}{\square}$

1 $\dfrac{2}{3} \times \dfrac{3}{4} \times \dfrac{4}{5}$ =

7 $\dfrac{2}{4} \times \dfrac{6}{8} \times \dfrac{10}{12}$ =

2 $\dfrac{3}{4} \times \dfrac{4}{5} \times \dfrac{5}{6}$ =

8 $\dfrac{2}{4} \times \dfrac{4}{6} \times \dfrac{6}{8}$ =

3 $\dfrac{1}{2} \times \dfrac{3}{4} \times \dfrac{5}{6}$ =

9 $\dfrac{1}{3} \times \dfrac{2}{4} \times \dfrac{3}{5}$ =

4 $\dfrac{2}{3} \times \dfrac{4}{5} \times \dfrac{6}{7}$ =

10 $\dfrac{1}{4} \times \dfrac{2}{5} \times \dfrac{3}{6}$ =

5 $\dfrac{5}{6} \times \dfrac{7}{8} \times \dfrac{9}{10}$ =

11 $\dfrac{1}{5} \times \dfrac{2}{6} \times \dfrac{3}{7} \times \dfrac{4}{8}$ =

6 $\dfrac{1}{2} \times \dfrac{4}{5} \times \dfrac{7}{8}$ =

12 The faces of a cuboid have areas $\dfrac{4}{15}$ cm², $\dfrac{25}{6}$ cm² and $\dfrac{9}{10}$ cm².

What is the volume of the cuboid?
What are the lengths of the edges?

C31 Multiplication: Decimals and fractions   NC

Decimals: Problem 0

> **0 a** $6 \times 2.73 =$

$6 \times 2.73 = 6 \times (273 \div 100) = (6 \times 273) \div 100.$

Work out 6×273 using short multiplication, then divide the answer by 100.

$$\begin{array}{r} 2\ 7\ 3 \\ \times\ \ \ \ 6 \\ \hline *\ *\ *\ * \end{array}$$

Work these out as efficiently as you can without using a *calculator*.

1 $7 \times 43.7 =$ **4** $0.0013 \times 0.076 =$ **7** $1.3 \times 0.076 =$

2 $0.53 \times 41.2 =$ **5** $0.6 \times 0.00273 =$ **8** $4.12 \times 5.3 =$

3 $0.053 \times 4.12 =$ **6** $0.007 \times 0.437 =$

> **9** Tony is paid £5.20 an hour. How much does he earn (before deductions) for a $42\frac{1}{2}$ hour working week?

Fractions: Problem 0

> **0 b** $1\frac{1}{2} \times 2\frac{2}{3} =$

When working with fractions in mathematics (after primary school) you should always change mixed fractions like $2\frac{2}{3}$ into $\frac{\text{numerator}}{\text{denominator}}$ form. Thus $2\frac{2}{3}$ should always be replaced by $\frac{\square}{3}$.

$$1\frac{1}{2} \times 2\frac{2}{3} = \frac{\square}{2} \times \frac{\square}{3} = \frac{\square}{\square}.$$

In the problems below, write each fraction in $\frac{\text{numerator}}{\text{denominator}}$ form.

Then simplify *using cancellation* (do *not* multiply out numerators and denominators separately).

10 $2\frac{4}{5} \times 40 =$ **12** $\frac{7}{13} \times 9\frac{3}{4} =$ **14** $\frac{12}{1001} \times \frac{143}{40} =$

11 $2\frac{4}{5} \times 2\frac{1}{2} =$ **13** $\frac{5}{99} \times \frac{54}{7} =$ **15** $\frac{84}{1001} \times \frac{13}{36} =$

> **16** Carpet underlay comes in rolls with a fixed width and costs £2.50 per metre. How much would you pay for 12.8 m?

Problem 0

> **0** Draw part of the number line from 0 to 5.   0 •————————————• 5
>
> **a** Mark the points 2 and 4. Mark the point halfway between 2 and 4. Which number is halfway between 2 and 4?
>
> **b** Mark the points $\frac{1}{2}$ and $\frac{1}{4}$. Mark the point halfway between $\frac{1}{2}$ and $\frac{1}{4}$. Which number is halfway between $\frac{1}{2}$ and $\frac{1}{4}$?

The first few questions may seem easy. But keep alert!

1 Which number is halfway between

    a 1 and 3   **b** 2 and 4   **c** 3 and 5?

2 Which number is halfway between

    a $\frac{1}{2}$ and $\frac{3}{2}$ **b** $\frac{2}{2}$ and $\frac{4}{2}$ **c** $\frac{3}{2}$ and $\frac{5}{2}$?

3 Which number is halfway between

    a $\frac{1}{4}$ and $\frac{3}{4}$ **b** $\frac{2}{4}$ and $\frac{4}{4}$ **c** $\frac{3}{4}$ and $\frac{5}{4}$?

4 Which number is

    a halfway between $\frac{1}{1}$ and $\frac{1}{3}$ (the answer is *not* $\frac{1}{2}$!)

    b halfway between $\frac{1}{2}$ and $\frac{1}{4}$ (the answer is *not* $\frac{1}{3}$!)

    c halfway between $\frac{1}{3}$ and $\frac{1}{5}$? (the answer is *not* $\frac{1}{4}$!)

5 Which number is halfway between

    a halfway between $\frac{2}{1}$ and $\frac{2}{3}$ (the answer is *not* $\frac{2}{2}$!)

    b halfway between $\frac{2}{2}$ and $\frac{2}{4}$ (the answer is *not* $\frac{2}{3}$!)

    c halfway between $\frac{2}{3}$ and $\frac{2}{5}$? (the answer is *not* $\frac{2}{5}$!)

6 Which number is halfway between

    a halfway between $\frac{4}{1}$ and $\frac{4}{3}$ (the answer is *not* $\frac{4}{2}$!)

    b halfway between $\frac{4}{2}$ and $\frac{4}{4}$ (the answer is *not* $\frac{4}{3}$!)

    c halfway between $\frac{4}{3}$ and $\frac{4}{5}$? (the answer is *not* $\frac{4}{4}$!)

Problems **1**, **2** and **3** are easy, but problems **4**, **5** and **6** are completely different. (However, you might not have noticed this without the warning in brackets. So keep your wits about you in the rest of this section.)

7 Which number is

   a halfway between $\frac{1}{5}$ and $\frac{1}{7}$ **b** halfway between $\frac{2}{3}$ and $\frac{4}{5}$?

8 a Joe scored $\frac{1}{3}$ of the marks on his first maths test and just $\frac{1}{5}$ of the marks on his second test. The two tests were equally important and had the same maximum mark. What fraction of the total marks on the two tests did Joe score?

   b Joanna scored $\frac{2}{3}$ of the marks on the first maths test and $\frac{2}{5}$ of the marks on the second test. What fraction of the total marks on the two tests did she score?

9 Which number is halfway between

a −3 and 5	**c** −1 and 3	**e** 2 and −4
b −2 and 4	**d** 3 and −5	**f** 1 and −3?

10 Which number is halfway between

a $-\frac{1}{3}$ and $\frac{1}{5}$	**c** $-\frac{1}{1}$ and $\frac{1}{3}$	**e** $\frac{1}{2}$ and $-\frac{1}{4}$
b $-\frac{1}{2}$ and $\frac{1}{4}$	**d** $\frac{1}{3}$ and $-\frac{1}{5}$	**f** $\frac{1}{1}$ and $-\frac{1}{3}$?

11 a Jack and Jill walked 1 mile up the hill at 3 mph to get a pail of water. Once they had filled their bucket, they walked back down the hill at 5 mph.

   i How long did they take to walk *up* the hill? (Give your answer in *hours*, as a *fraction*, not in minutes.)

   ii How long did they take to walk *down* the hill? (Give your answer in *hours*, as a *fraction*, not in minutes.)

   iii Ignoring the time taken to fill up their bucket, what was their average speed for the complete journey – up and down?

   b What if they had walked up the hill at 2 mph and down the hill at 4 mph. What would their average speed have been for the complete journey up and down?

Here is another way of thinking about problems like **1–10** above.
To find the point halfway between 3 and 5:
   Start at 3.
   Then 'move on *half the distance from 3 to 5*': that is,
   $\frac{1}{2} \times (5-3)$.

   $\therefore$ The number halfway between 3 and 5 is: $3 + \frac{1}{2}(5-3) = \underline{}$.

12 a What is the distance between 3 and 5?

So the number halfway between 3 and 5 is $3 + \frac{1}{2}(5 - 3) =$

b What is the distance between -3 and 5?

So the number halfway between -3 and 5 is $(-3) + \frac{1}{2}(5 - (-3)) =$

c What is the distance between 3 and -5?

So the number halfway between 3 and -5 is $(-5) + \frac{1}{2}(3 - (-5)) =$

d What is the distance between $\frac{1}{3}$ and $\frac{1}{5}$?

So the number halfway between $\frac{1}{3}$ and $\frac{1}{5}$ is $\frac{1}{5} + \frac{1}{2}\left(\frac{1}{3} - \frac{1}{5}\right) =$

e What is the distance between $\frac{1}{3}$ and $-\frac{1}{5}$?

So the number halfway between $\frac{1}{3}$ and $-\frac{1}{5}$ is

$-\frac{1}{5} + \frac{1}{2}\left(\frac{1}{3} - \left(-\frac{1}{5}\right)\right) =$

f What is the distance between $-\frac{1}{3}$ and $\frac{1}{5}$?

So the number halfway between $-\frac{1}{3}$ and $\frac{1}{5}$ is

$-\frac{1}{3} + \frac{1}{2}\left(\frac{1}{5} - \left(-\frac{1}{3}\right)\right) =$

The number halfway between x and y is $x + \frac{1}{2}(y - x) = \frac{1}{2}(x + y)$.

The number halfway between x and y is the *average (mean)* of x and y.

Use this idea to answer the following questions quickly and correctly. (Where a question looks familiar, *don't* just repeat the answer you gave the first time. Work it out again *using the '$\frac{1}{2}(x + y)$' method.*)

13 Which number is halfway between

a $\frac{1}{3}$ and $\frac{1}{5}$

b $\frac{1}{5}$ and $\frac{1}{7}$

c $\frac{1}{4}$ and $\frac{1}{7}$

d $\frac{1}{2}$ and $\frac{1}{4}$

e $\frac{1}{1}$ and $\frac{1}{3}$

f $\frac{2}{3}$ and $\frac{4}{5}$

g $-\frac{1}{2}$ and $\frac{1}{4}$

h $-\frac{1}{1}$ and $\frac{1}{3}$

i $\frac{1}{2}$ and $-\frac{1}{4}$

j $\frac{1}{1}$ and $-\frac{1}{3}$

k $\frac{1}{3}$ and $-\frac{1}{5}$

l $\frac{5}{4}$ and $-\frac{1}{2}$

m $-\frac{1}{3}$ and $\frac{1}{5}$

n $-\frac{4}{3}$ and $\frac{7}{8}$

o $-\frac{3}{4}$ and $\frac{4}{3}$

p -5 and $\frac{1}{5}$

q $-\frac{1}{2}$ and -7

r $\frac{9}{5}$ and $-\frac{1}{3}$

s $\frac{17}{5}$ and 5?

C33 Division: Fractions and decimals

NC

Division of fractions: Problem 0

> **0 a i** $\frac{3}{4} \div \frac{5}{4} =$ **ii** $\frac{3}{4} \div \frac{5}{6} =$

Division of fractions is easy if (as in problem **0ai**) the denominators are the same.

$$\frac{3}{4} = 3 \times \frac{1}{4} \text{ and } \frac{5}{4} = 5 \times \frac{1}{4} \qquad \therefore \frac{\frac{3}{4}}{\frac{5}{4}} = \frac{\square \times \frac{1}{4}}{\square \times \frac{1}{4}} = \frac{\square}{\square}$$

If the denominators are different rewrite the two fractions in the numerator and the denominator so that they have the *same* denominator. Then cancel.

$$\frac{\frac{3}{4}}{\frac{5}{6}} = \frac{\frac{\square}{12}}{\frac{\square}{12}} = \frac{\square \times \frac{1}{12}}{\square \times \frac{1}{12}} = \frac{\square}{\square}$$

1 $\frac{1}{4} \div \frac{1}{3} =$ **4** $\frac{7}{4} \div \frac{7}{3} =$

2 $1\frac{1}{2} \div \frac{3}{4} =$ **5** $\frac{7}{6} \div \frac{4}{15} =$

3 $2\frac{3}{4} \div 4\frac{1}{8} =$ **6** $\frac{6}{55} \div \frac{3}{25} =$

> **7** A rectangle has width $\frac{4}{5}$ cm and area $\frac{1}{3}$ cm².
> What is its length?

Division of decimals: Problem 0

> **0 b** $0.372 \div 1.2 =$

To work out $0.372 \div 1.2$:
>   First make sure that you know how to divide by an integer;
>   then use reverse cancellation to change division by a decimal into
>   division by an integer.

CORE

157

Remember that $0.372 \div 1.2 = \dfrac{0.372}{\square} = \dfrac{0.372 \times 10}{\underline{} \times 10} = \dfrac{\square}{12}$

Then carry out the division of the decimal 3.72 by the *integer* 12 to get the answer.

$$12 \overline{)\, 3.7\,2}^{\,0.}$$

8 $0.36 \div 1.2 = \dfrac{0.36}{1.2} = \dfrac{3.6}{12} =$

9 $0.001\,08 \div 0.12 =$

10 $15.45 \div 0.003 =$

11 $6.100\,36 \div 0.07 =$

12 $0.004\,082 \div 0.013 =$

13 You are given a strip of wood 2.713 m long. You have to cut this long strip into as many shorter strips, each of length 0.14 m, as possible.
How many shorter strips do you get and how long is the piece left over?

C34 A formula for primes? NC

Prime numbers play a central role in mathematics – so it is natural to try to find a recipe, or formula, that will produce prime numbers. If we knew a bit more about prime numbers we might know whether it is reasonable to expect such a formula, or whether such a formula is rather unlikely! Meanwhile it is an interesting exercise to see how good (or how bad) some simple formulae are at producing primes.

Problem 0

0 **a** Substitute the values $n = 1$, $n = 2$, $n = 3$, $n = 4$, and so on in turn into the formula
  $$p(n) = 2n + 1.$$
  You should get all o** numbers, starting with ___.

  The first three values 3, 5, 7 happen to be **i*e numbers; but the fourth value, 9, isn't.
  So the formula 'works' for $n \leq 3$, but breaks down when $n = 4$.

  b What is the smallest value of n for which the formula
  $$p(n) = 4n^2 + 1$$
  fails to produce a prime number?

For each formula, find the smallest positive integer, n, for which the given formula for $p(n)$ *fails* to produce a prime number.

1 $p(n) = n^2 + n + 1$ **4** $p(n) = n^2 + n + 11$ **7** $p(n) = n^2 - n + 17$ **10** $p(n) = n^2 + n + 41$

2 $p(n) = n^2 + 3n + 1$ **5** $p(n) = n^2 - n + 11$ **8** $p(n) = n^2 + n + 31$ **11** $p(n) = n^2 - n + 41$

3 $p(n) = 2n^2 + 2n + 7$ **6** $p(n) = n^2 + n + 17$ **9** $p(n) = n^2 - n + 31$ **12** $p(n) = n^3 + n + 11$

13 Let $p(n) = n^2 - n + 3$.   Calculate $p(n)$ when $n = 1$ and when $n = 2$.
  Notice that $p(n) = n^2 - n + 3$, so when $n = 3$,
    $$p(n) = p(3) = 3 \times 3 - 3 + 3 = 3(3 - 1 + 1) = 3 \times 3 \text{ is a multiple of } 3.$$

  a Let $p(n) = n^2 - n + 11$.
    What value of n guarantees that $p(n)$ will be a multiple of 11?

  b Let $p(n) = n^2 - n + 17$.
    What value of n guarantees that $p(n)$ will be a multiple of 17?

14 Let $p(n) = n^2 + 3n + 1$.

  a When $n = 6$,
    n^2 has units digit ___ and $3n$ has units digit ___
    $\therefore p(n) = n^2 + 3n + 1$ has units digit ___ $\therefore p(n)$ is a multiple of ___.

  b By part **a** you can be sure that $p(n)$ cannot be a prime number when $n = 6$,
    or when $n = 16$, or when $n = 26$, or ___. Is it perhaps true that $p(n)$
    gives a prime number for all *other* values of n? If not, what is the first
    other value of n for which $p(n)$ fails to produce a prime number?

C35 Negative numbers NC

CORE

Given any number x, its *negative*, $-x$, is the number which when added to x gives 0.

If x is *negative* to start with, then *its* negative, $-x$, is *positive!*

$$-2 + 2 = 0$$
$$\therefore \text{ The negative of } -2 \text{ must be } 2$$
$$\therefore -(-2) = 2$$

Similarly
$$-\left(-\tfrac{1}{2}\right) + \left(-\tfrac{1}{2}\right) = 0 = \tfrac{1}{2} + \left(-\tfrac{1}{2}\right)$$
$$\therefore -\left(-\tfrac{1}{2}\right) = \tfrac{1}{2}$$

Problem 0

0 a i $5 + (-7)$ =	**ii** $4 - (-11)$ =
b i $3a + (-5a)$ =	**ii** $6y - (-5y)$ =

If you are unsure about how to answer any of these problems, go back to moving *to the right* to add, and moving *to the left* to subtract, on the number line:

◎ $4 + 11$ means start at 4, and move 11 units to the *i***

◎ $4 - 11$ means start at 4, and then move 11 units to the *e**

◎ $4 + (-11)$ means start at 4, and move -11 units to the *i***
   (that is, move 11 units to the *e**)

◎ $(-4) + (-11)$ means start at -4, and move 11 units to the *e**

1 Calculate

a $3 + (-2)$ =		**i** $3a + (-2a)$ =
b $3 + (-6)$ =		**j** $3a + (-6a)$ =
c $3 + 5$ =		**k** $3a + 5a$ =
d $3 + (-3)$ =		**l** $3a + (-3a)$ =
e $(-4) + (-1)$ =		**m** $(-4a) + (-a)$ =
f $(-4) + (-6)$ =		**n** $(-4a) + (-6a)$ =
g $(-4) + 6$ =		**o** $(-4a) + 6a$ =
h $(-4) + (-4)$ =		**p** $(-4a) + (-4a)$ =

2 Calculate

a $5 + (-3) =$ **i** $5x - (-3x) =$

b $5 - 3 =$ **j** $(-5x) - (-3x) =$

c $(-5) - (-3) =$ **k** $5x - 3x =$

d $(-5) - 3 =$ **l** $(-5x) - 3x =$

e $7 - (-11) =$ **m** $(-7x) - 11x =$

f $7 - 11 =$ **n** $7x - 11x =$

g $(-7) - 11 =$ **o** $(-7x) - (-11x) =$

h $(-7) - (-11) =$ **p** $7x - (-11x) =$

3 Put the correct number in each equation.

a $17 + \_\_\_ = 23$ **i** $5 + \_\_\_ - 8 = -7$

b $17 + \_\_\_ = -23$ **j** $5 + \_\_\_ - 8 = 7$

c $(-17) + \_\_\_ = -23$ **k** $(-5) + \_\_\_ - 8 = -7$

d $(-17) + \_\_\_ = 23$ **l** $(-5) + \_\_\_ - 8 = 7$

e $\_\_\_ + 24 = 18$ **m** $5 + \_\_\_ + 8 = -7$

f $\_\_\_ + 24 = -18$ **n** $5 + \_\_\_ + 8 = 7$

g $\_\_\_ - 24 = 18$ **o** $(-5) + \_\_\_ + 8 = -7$

h $\_\_\_ - 24 = -18$ **p** $(-5) + \_\_\_ + 8 = 7$

4 Find the value of each expression when $s = 3$ and $t = -2$.

a $s + t =$ **d** $(-s) + t =$

b $s - t =$ **e** $s + (-t) =$

c $(-s) - t =$ **f** $(-s) - (-t) =$

5 Calculate

a $\frac{3}{4} + \frac{1}{2}$ **g** $\frac{2}{3} + \frac{3}{4}$

b $\frac{3}{4} - \frac{1}{2}$ **h** $\left(-\frac{2}{3}\right) + \frac{3}{4}$

c $\left(-\frac{3}{4}\right) + \frac{1}{2}$ **i** $\frac{4}{5} + \left(-\frac{1}{2}\right)$

d $\left(-\frac{3}{4}\right) - \frac{1}{2}$ **j** $\frac{4}{5} - \left(-\frac{1}{2}\right)$

e $\frac{2}{3} - \frac{3}{4}$ **k** $\frac{4}{5} + \left(-\frac{4}{5}\right)$

f $\left(-\frac{2}{3}\right) - \frac{3}{4}$ **l** $\frac{4}{5} - \left(-\frac{4}{5}\right)$

C36 Word sums *B*

In a *word sum* each letter stands for one of the digits 0–9. Different letters
stand for different digits, and each letter stands for the same digit each
time it occurs. None of the integers in a word sum starts with a '0'. Your
job is to work out which digits the different letters could stand for
(if possible using logic rather than guesswork).

◎   A given word sum may be impossible (in which case you
    have to explain why it cannot have a solution)

◎   it may have just one solution (in which case you find that
    solution and prove that it is the only one)

◎   it may have several solutions (in which case you need to find
    them all and prove that you have found them all).

Problem 0

> **0 Decide whether each of the following word sums has a solution
> and explain why.**
>
> **a**   O N E   **b**   N I N E
>   **+ E L E V E N**   **+ T H R E E**
>   **T W E L V E**   **T W E L V E**

For each word sum, decide whether it has a solution, and *explain
why* (or why not).

1   F O R T Y   **5**   T H R E E   **9**   O N E
    + F O R T Y   **+ E I G H T**   **+ S E V E N**
    E I G H T Y   **E L E V E N**   **E I G H T**

2   F O U R   **6**   F O U R   **10**   F I V E
    + S E V E N   **+ E I G H T**   **+ T H R E E**
    E L E V E N   **T W E L V E**   **E I G H T**

3   F I V E   **7**   E I G H T   **11**   T H I S
    +   T W O   **+ T W E L V E**   **+ O N E 'S**
    S E V E N   **T W E N T Y**   **A W F U L**

4   F O U R   **8**   N I N E
    + F I V E   **+ E L E V E N**
    N I N E   **T W E N T Y**

C37 Adding and subtracting fractions *B*

Problem 0

0 a $\frac{3}{4} + \frac{2}{3} =$	**b** $\frac{3}{4} - \frac{2}{3} =$

$\frac{3}{4}$ = '3 lots of $\frac{1}{4}$' = $3 \times \frac{1}{4}$ $\frac{5}{6}$ = '5 lots of $\frac{1}{6}$' = $5 \times \frac{1}{6}$

Adding fractions *with the same denominator* is easy.

$$\frac{3}{4} + \frac{5}{4} = 3 \times \frac{1}{4} + 5 \times \frac{1}{4} = \underline{\quad} \times \frac{1}{4} = \underline{\quad}$$

To add two fractions *with different denominators*, rewrite the fractions so that they have the *same* denominator. To rewrite $\frac{3}{4}$ and $\frac{5}{6}$ with a common denominator you need to think

$$lcm(4, 6) = \underline{\quad}$$
$$= 4 \times \underline{\quad} = 6 \times \underline{\quad}$$
$$\therefore \frac{1}{4} = \frac{\square}{4 \times 3} \text{ and } \frac{1}{6} = \frac{\square}{6 \times 2}$$
$$\therefore \frac{3}{4} + \frac{5}{6} = 3 \times \frac{1}{4} + 5 \times \frac{1}{6}$$
$$= 3 \times \frac{3}{12} + 5 \times \frac{2}{12} = \frac{\square}{12}$$

In short: $\frac{3}{4} + \frac{5}{6} = \frac{3 \times 3}{4 \times 3} + \frac{5 \times 2}{6 \times 2}$
$$= \frac{9}{12} + \frac{10}{12} = \frac{\square}{12} = \frac{\square}{\square}$$

1 Give each answer *in fully simplified form.*

a $\frac{1}{6} + \frac{5}{6} =$ **f** $\frac{3}{20} + \frac{5}{20} =$ **k** $\frac{13}{18} + \frac{11}{18} =$

b $\frac{1}{8} + \frac{3}{8} =$ **g** $\frac{13}{20} + \frac{11}{20} =$ **l** $\frac{13}{16} + \frac{11}{16} =$

c $\frac{3}{12} + \frac{5}{12} =$ **h** $\frac{5}{6} + \frac{4}{6} =$ **m** $\frac{13}{21} + \frac{8}{21} =$

d $\frac{3}{16} + \frac{5}{16} =$ **i** $\frac{7}{8} + \frac{5}{8} =$ **n** $\frac{5}{21} + \frac{2}{21} =$

e $\frac{2}{20} + \frac{3}{20} =$ **j** $\frac{13}{12} + \frac{5}{12} =$

2 Give each answer in fully simplified form.

a $\dfrac{1}{2}+\dfrac{2}{3}$ = ___ + ___ =

h $\dfrac{5}{6}+\dfrac{3}{8}$ = ___ + ___ =

b $\dfrac{1}{3}+\dfrac{3}{4}$ = ___ + ___ =

i $\dfrac{7}{8}-\dfrac{3}{10}$ = ___ − ___ =

c $\dfrac{2}{5}+\dfrac{3}{4}$ = ___ + ___ =

j $\dfrac{5}{16}+\dfrac{3}{12}$ = ___ + ___ =

d $\dfrac{3}{2}+\dfrac{3}{5}$ = ___ + ___ =

k $\dfrac{4}{15}+\dfrac{11}{20}$ = ___ + ___ =

e $\dfrac{3}{10}+\dfrac{2}{15}$ = ___ + ___ =

l $\dfrac{13}{21}-\dfrac{5}{14}$ = ___ − ___ =

f $\dfrac{5}{6}+\dfrac{3}{4}$ = ___ + ___ =

m $\dfrac{13}{4}+\dfrac{9}{22}$ = ___ + ___ =

g $\dfrac{5}{12}+\dfrac{7}{15}$ = ___ + ___ =

n $\dfrac{7}{30}-\dfrac{2}{21}$ = ___ − ___ =

3 Give each answer in fully simplified form.

a $1-\dfrac{1}{2}-\dfrac{1}{6}$ =

f $\dfrac{5a}{6}-\dfrac{3a}{4}$ =

b $\dfrac{7}{10}-\dfrac{2}{5}+\dfrac{5}{2}$ =

g $\dfrac{a^2}{4}-\dfrac{a^2}{6}$ =

c $\dfrac{4}{3}-\dfrac{5}{6}-\dfrac{1}{2}$ =

h $\dfrac{7a}{10}-\dfrac{2a}{5}$ =

d $\dfrac{a}{2}+\dfrac{a}{3}$ =

i $\dfrac{ab}{4}-\dfrac{ab}{6}$ =

e $\dfrac{a}{2}+\dfrac{b}{3}$ =

j $\dfrac{6}{a}-\dfrac{4}{a}$ =

4 Fill in the empty squares to make all the equations in this grid correct both horizontally and vertically. Enter each fraction in its simplest form.

	+		=	$\dfrac{15}{16}$
+		+		+
$\dfrac{3}{8}$	+	$\dfrac{1}{4}$	=	
=		=		=
	+	$\dfrac{9}{16}$	=	

You need the SAS and ASA congruence criteria for triangles.

Problem 0

0 Take a sheet of 1 cm square dotty paper.
Mark the origin $O = (0, 0)$.
Mark the x-axis and the y-axis.

a Mark the following points A–S.

A:(4, 0)	E:(12, 12)	I:(10, 0)	M:(6, −7)	Q:(0, −17)
B:(0, −6)	F:(5, 12)	J:(0, 8)	N:(8, −6)	R:(0, −8)
C:(7, 4)	G:(0, 4)	K:(−4, 3)	O:(0, 0)	S:(−6, 0)
D:(0, 13)	H:(3, 3)	L:(5, −3)	P:(−7, −7)	

b Where three or more of the points A–S are **collinear** (that is, lie on the same straight line), explain how you can be sure, and draw the line.

c Where you can be sure that two points, X, Y, among the points A–S are *exactly* the same distance from the origin O, explain why OX = OY, and draw the circle with centre O through the two points, X, Y.

1 Mark four points A, B, C, D on square dotty paper as shown. Copy and complete the steps in the following proof.

Claim ABCD is a ___.

Proof Let X and Y be the points where the horizontal line through B meets the vertical lines through A and C respectively.
    ∠AXB = ___
∴ ∠XAB + ∠XBA = ___ (since angles in △XAB add to ___)
Now AX = BY = ___, ∠AXB = ∠BYC = ___, and XB = YC = ___;
∴ △AXB is congruent to △BYC (by the ___ congruence criterion)
∴ △AXB and △BYC are equal in all respects,
    so AB = BC, and ∠YBC = ∠ ___.
∴∠YBC + ∠XBA = ___
∴ ∠ABC = ___ (since the ∠XBA + ∠ABC + ∠CBY form a ___ angle)
Similarly BC = CD and ∠BCD = ___
        CD = DA and ∠CDA = ___
∴ ABCD is a ___.   **QED**

CORE

2 a For the two points $O = (0, 0)$ and $J = (12, 20)$ *both* their coordinates are integers.
How many other points on the line *segment* OJ have both coordinates integers?

b Let K be the point $(36, 90)$.
How many other points on the line segment OK have both coordinates integers?
What are they?

c Let L be the point $(48, 72)$.
How many other points on the line segment OL have both coordinates integers?
What are they?

d Let M be the point $(120, 168)$.
How many other points on the line segment OM have both coordinates integers?
What are they?

e Let $N = (7, 3)$ and $P = (31, 43)$.
How many other points on the line segment NP have both coordinates integers? What are they?

f Let $Q = (-11, 13)$ and $R = (49, 97)$.
How many other points on the line segment QR have both coordinates integers? What are they?

g Let $S = (23, -15)$ and $T = (47, 21)$.
How many other points on the line segment ST have both coordinates integers? What are they?

h Let $U = (-20, 11)$ and $V = (304, 191)$.
How many other points on the line segment UV have both coordinates integers? What are they?

i Let $W = (57, 3)$ and $X = (300, 300)$.
How many other points on the line segment WX have both coordinates integers? What are they?

j Let $Y = (96, 81)$ and $Z = (600, 900)$.
How many points on the line segment YZ have both coordinates integers? What are they?

3 Write each of these fractions in its simplest form.

a $\dfrac{20}{12}$ **c** $\dfrac{72}{48}$ **e** $\dfrac{40}{24}$ **g** $\dfrac{36}{24}$ **i** $\dfrac{297}{243}$

b $\dfrac{90}{36}$ **d** $\dfrac{168}{120}$ **f** $\dfrac{84}{60}$ **h** $\dfrac{180}{324}$ **j** $\dfrac{819}{504}$

Given any line segment *AB*, there is an easy way to calculate the coordinates of the mid-point *M* of *AB*.

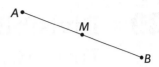

4 **Given** two points, *A*, *B*, with *M* the mid-point of *AB*.
   Prove The *x*- and *y*-coordinates of *M* are the a∗e∗a∗e∗ of the *x*- and *y*-coordinates of *A* and *B*.

   Copy and complete the following proof. Then use the result to complete problem **5**.

   Proof
   Construct lines through *A* and *B* parallel to the *x*-axis, and the line through *M* parallel to the *y*-axis.
   Let these lines meet at *U* and *V* as shown on the right.

   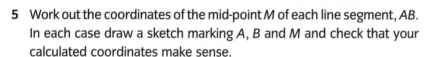

   Then ∠*UMA* = ∠*VMB* (∗e∗∗i∗a∗∗∗ o∗∗o∗i∗e angles)
   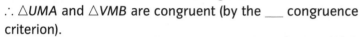
               AM = *BM* (given, since *M* is the ∗i∗∗oi∗∗ of *AB*)
        ∠*MAU* = ∠*MBV* (a∗∗e∗∗a∗e angles)
   ∴ △*UMA* and △*VMB* are congruent (by the ___ congruence criterion).
   ∴ *AU* = *BV*, so the *x*-coordinates of *U*, *V* and *M* (which are all equal) are all equal to the a∗e∗a∗e of the *x*-coordinates of *A* and *B*.
   Also *UM* = *VM*, so the *y*-coordinate of *M* is the a∗e∗a∗e of the *y*-coordinates of *A* and *B*.

5 Work out the coordinates of the mid-point *M* of each line segment, *AB*.
   In each case draw a sketch marking *A*, *B* and *M* and check that your calculated coordinates make sense.

   a *A* = (1, 0),   *B* = (5, 0)
   b *A* = (0, −1), *B* = (0, 3)
   c *A* = (0, 3),   *B* = (1, 5)
   d *A* = (4, 3),   *B* = (9, 6)

   e *A* = (−1, 3), *B* = (2, −4)
   f *A* = (−5, 7), *B* = (1, 11)
   g *A* = (1, −3), *B* = (−6, −7)
   h *A* = (1, −3), *B* = (−4, 5)

C39 Divisibility *B*: Does it go? **NC**
How do you know?

CORE

In Section **T27** *Divisibility A* we reviewed how to tell when an integer is divisible by 2, by 5 and by 10. We also looked at divisibility by 4 and by 8.

Fact An integer is divisible by 4 *precisely when* the two-digit number formed by the *e** and u*i** digits is a multiple of 4.

More precisely, when you divide an integer by 4, the *e*ai**e* is the same as the *e*ai**e* you get when you divide the two-digit integer formed by the tens and units digits by 4.

$1357 = 13 \times 100 + 57 = 13 \times (25 \times 4) + 57$
$$= (13 \times 25) \times 4 + 57$$
$$= (13 \times 25) \times 4 + (14 \times 4 + 1)$$
$$\therefore \textit{remainder } 1$$

Fact. An integer is divisible by 8 *precisely when* the ***ee-digit number formed by the *u***e**, *e**, and u*i** digits is a multiple of 8.

More precisely, when you divide an integer by 8, the *e*ai**e* is the same as the *e*ai**e* you get when you divide the three-digit integer formed by the hundreds, tens and units digits by 8.

$1357 = 1 \times 1000 + 357 = 125 \times 8 + 357$
$$= 125 \times 8 + (44 \times 8 + 5) \therefore \textit{remainder } 5$$

This section looks at how you can tell when a given integer is divisible by 3, by 6, or by 9.

Problem 0

> **0 a** Use short division to find the remainder when you divide each of the following integers by 3.
>
> **i** 78: remainder ___   **iv** 357: remainder ___
>
> **ii** 198: remainder ___   **v** 7203: remainder ___
>
> **iii** 308: remainder ___   **vi** 123456: remainder ___

b Now add the digits of each integer to find the digit-sum; then find the remainder when you divide this digit-sum by 3.

i 78: digit-sum = ___,   remainder =

ii 198: digit-sum = ___,   remainder =

iii 308: digit-sum = ___,   remainder =

iv 357: digit-sum = ___,   remainder =

v 7203: digit-sum = ___,   remainder =

vi 123456: digit-sum = ___,   remainder =

c Make a guess about how to find the remainder when you divide an integer by 3.

1 a Use the rule you guessed in problem **0c** to write what you expect to be the remainder when you divide each of these integers by 3 *without carrying out the division*.

i 94: remainder = ___   iv 345: remainder = ___

ii 23 458: remainder = ___   v 123 456: remainder = ___

iii 1 234 321: remainder = ___   vi 23 454: remainder = ___

b Fill in the missing details in the following *justification* of your guessed rule.

Question How can you find quickly the remainder when you divide 1234 by 3?

Answer Split up $N = 1234$ into separate powers of 10
$$N = 1234 = 1 \times 1000 + \underline{} \times 100 + \underline{} \times 10 + 4$$

Then replace 10 by $(9 + 1)$, 100 by $(99 + 1)$, and so on
$$N = 1234 = 1 \times (\underline{} + 1) + 2 \times (99 + 1) + 3 \times (\underline{} + 1) + 4$$

Collect all the 9s, 99s and 999s together at the end and the other terms $(1 \times 1 = 1, 2 \times 1 = 2, 3 \times 1 = 3, 4)$ at the front:
$$N = 1234 = (1 + 2 + 3 + 4) + (999 + 2 \times 99 + 3 \times 9)$$

Finally notice that 999, 99, and 9 are all exactly divisible by ___.
∴ $(999 + 2 \times 99 + 3 \times 9)$ contributes nothing to the *e*ai**e* when you divide by **3**.

∴ The remainder when you divide $N = 1234$ by **3** is the same as the remainder when you divide $1 + 2 + 3 + 4$ by **3**.   **QED**

2 *Without carrying out the division*, write down the remainder when you divide each of these integers by 3.

    a 456 789   remainder = ___   **d** 765 432   remainder = ___

    b 234 567   remainder = ___   **e** 123 456 789   remainder = ___

    c 987 654   remainder = ___   **f** 13 579   remainder = ___

Question How can you tell quickly when a given integer N is divisible by 6?

Any multiple of 6 is a multiple of 2×3, so must be both a multiple of ___ *and* a multiple of ___.

On the other hand, any integer N that is a multiple of 2 is equal to
    '2 × (something)', or $2 \times n$.
If the same integer N is a multiple of 3, it must also be equal to
    '3 × (something else)', or $3 \times m$.
So $2 \times n$ and $3 \times m$ are different ways of writing the same integer N.
    $\therefore N = 2 \times n = 3 \times m$, where n and m are unknown integers.
    $\therefore 3 \times m$ is even, so m must be even
    $\therefore N = 3 \times m$ is a multiple of 6.

Answer N is a multiple of $6 = 2 \times 3$ *precisely when* N is a multiple of 2 and also a multiple of 3.

3 Use this rule to decide quickly which of the following integers are divisible by 6 *without carrying out the division*.

    a 94   **d** 345   **g** 456 789   **j** 765 432

    b 23 458   **e** 123 456   **h** 234 567   **k** 123 456 789

    c 1 234 321   **f** 23 454   **i** 987 654   **l** 13 579

In fact, when you divide N by 6, the *remainder* is completely determined by the remainders you get when you divide N by 2 and by 3 separately.

> For example, suppose $N = 1234$.
> The units digit of N is even, so when you divide N by 2 the remainder is **0**.
> (Digit-sum of N) = $1 + 2 + 3 + 4 = 3 \times 3 + 1$ so when you divide N by 3 the remainder is **1**.
> $\therefore$ when you divide $N = 1234$ by 6 (= 2×3) *the remainder must be 4 (Why '4'?).*

In general you need to think carefully to find the remainder when you divide by 6.

For example, when $N = 1235$, when you divide N by **2** the remainder is **1**.

(Digit-sum of N) $= 1 + 2 + 3 + 5 = 3 \times 3 + 2$, so when you divide N by **3** the remainder is 2.

$\therefore$ when you divide $N = 1235$ by **6** the remainder must satisfy *two conditions*:

    i it must be *odd* and **ii** it must be *2 more than a multiple of 3*.

$\therefore$ when you divide $N = 1235$ by **6** *the remainder must be 5.*

---

4 a Without carrying out the division, write down the remainder when you divide each of these integers by 6.

i 94	**v** 123 456	**ix** 987 654
ii 23 458	**vi** 23 454	**x** 765 432
iii 1 234 321	**vii** 456 789	**xi** 123 456 789
iv 345	**viii** 234 567	**xii** 13 579

b Without carrying out the division, write down the remainder when you divide each of these integers by 6.

i 96	**iii** 23 456	**v** 12 345
ii 187	**iv** 45 754	**vi** 4343

Question How can you tell whether the integer N is divisible by 9?

Answer N is a multiple of 9 *precisely when* the digit-sum of N is a multiple of 9.

For example

a Suppose $N = 12345678$.

$\therefore$ (digit-sum of N) $= 1 + 2 + 3 + 4 + 5 + 6 + 7 + 8 = \mathbf{36}$, so $N = 12345678$ **is** exactly divisible by 9

b Suppose $N = 2468$.

$\therefore$ (digit-sum of N) $= 2 + 4 + 6 + 8 = \mathbf{20}$, so $N = 2468$ is *not* exactly divisible by 9.

In fact, when you divide N by 9, the *remainder* is the same as the remainder you get when you divide the *digit-sum of N* by 9.

For example, suppose $N = 1234$

$\therefore$ (digit-sum of N) $= 1 + 2 + 3 + 4 = 1 \times 9 + 1$

$\therefore$ the remainder when you divide $N = 1234$ by 9 is 1.

5 a Use the rule on the previous page to write down quickly, *without carrying out the division*, the exact remainder when you divide each of these integers by 9.

   i 94   **iii** 1 234 321   **v** 123 456

   ii 23 458   **iv** 345   **vi** 23 454

b Fill in the missing details in the following *justification* of this rule.

Split up $N = 1234$ into separate powers of 10:

$$N = 1234 = 1 \times 1000 + \_\_\_ \times 100 + \_\_\_ \times 10 + 4$$

Then replace 10 by $(9 + 1)$, 100 by $(99 + 1)$, and so on

$$N = 1234 = 1 \times (\_\_\_ + 1) + 2 \times (99 + 1) + 3 \times (\_\_\_ + 1) + 4$$

Collect the 9s, 99s and 999s together at the end and the other terms 1×1, 2×1, 3×1, **4** at the front:

$$N = 1234 = (1 + 2 + 3 + 4) + (999 + 2 \times 99 + 3 \times 9)$$

Finally notice that 999, 99, and 9 are all exactly divisible by ___, so $(999 + 2 \times 99 + 3 \times 9)$ contributes nothing to the remainder when you divide by **9**.

$\therefore$ The remainder when you divide $N = 1234$ by **9** is the same as the remainder when you divide $1 + 2 + 3 + 4$ by **9**.   **QED**

You now have simple ways of testing for divisibility by 2, by 3, by 4, by 5, by 6, by 8, by 9, and by 10. You might like to look up (and justify) a simple test for divisibility by 11, and a slightly more complicated test for divisibility by 7. See *Maths Challenge 3*, Section 6, (Oxford University Press 2000) for a glimpse of divisibility tests for 7, 13, and 19.

E1 More missing digits NC

The logic behind the arithmetical algorithms for addition, subtraction, multiplication and division leads *from* the given starting numbers *to* the answer. But if you understand what is really going on, and are willing to *think*, you should be able to work backwards and fill in the missing digits.

1 Find all solutions to this multiplication and prove that you have found them all.

```
      2 *
   ×    *
   ─────
   2 * 4
```

2 Find all solutions to this multiplication and prove that you have found them all.

```
      * *
   ×    6
   ─────
   3 * 2
```

3 Find all solutions to this multiplication and prove that you have found them all.

```
    * 6 *
   ×    *
   ─────
   4 * 5
```

4 Find all solutions to this multiplication and prove that you have found them all.

```
    * 6 *
   ×      *
   ───────
   * 7 * 3
```

5 Use the digits 1, 2, 3, 4, 5, 6 once each to complete this multiplication.
   Explain why there is only one solution.

```
      * *
   ×    *
   ─────
   * * *
```

6 Find all solutions to this multiplication.
   Explain clearly how you can be sure that you have found all solutions.

```
       2 * *
   ×     9 *
   ─────────
     * * * 7
   * * 4 9 *
   ─────────
   * * * * *
```

7 Is it possible to use the digits 1–7, once each, to complete this multiplication?
   Justify your answer.

```
      * * *
   ×      *
   ─────
   * * *
```

173

E2 Divisibility problems NC

EXTENSION

This sections uses and extends the results derived in Section **C41**.

1 *Without doing the division* write down the remainder when each of these integers is divided by 9.

    a 369   **d** 135   **g** 246   **j** 1234

    b 963   **e** 531   **h** 642   **k** 2413

    c 693   **f** 315   **i** 426   **l** 2341

2 *Without doing the division* decide which of these integers is an exact multiple of 6.

    a 123   **d** 234   **g** 12 345   **j** 15 324

    b 312   **e** 342   **h** 54 312   **k** 52 413

    c 132   **f** 243   **i** 43 512   **l** 31 542

3 *Without doing the division* decide which of these integers is an exact multiple of 18.

    a 132   **d** 324   **g** 2340   **j** 3024

    b 234   **e** 342   **h** 2403   **k** 4023

    c 414   **f** 240   **i** 4032   **l** 4032

4 **a** **i** Without doing the division, find the remainder when 853 is divided by 9.

    ii Without doing the division, find the remainder when 358 is divided by 9.

    iii Without evaluating 853 − 358 explain why the answer must be divisible by 9.

   b Now do the division and complete the equation

       853 − 358 = 9 × ___

5 **a** Without doing the division explain why 9876 − 6789 must be divisible by 9.

   b Now do the division and complete the equation

       9876 − 6789 = 9 × ___

6 Complete each of these equations.

    a 1 − 1   = 11 × ___   **d** 1000 + 1   = 11 × ___

    b 10 + 1 = 11 × ___   **e** 10 000 − 1 = 11 × ___

    c 100 − 1 = 11 × ___   **f** 100 000 + 1 = 11 × ___

The next problem invites you to imitate C39, problem 5b to explain the following test for divisibility by 11.

Claim N is a multiple of 11 *precisely when* the *alternating digit sum* is a multiple of 11.

For example

◎ Suppose $N = 95\,359$.

∴ (alternating digit sum of N) = $9 - 5 + 3 - 5 + 9 = 11$
∴ $N = 95\,359$ *is* exactly divisible by 11.

◎ Suppose $N = 10\,376$.

∴ (alternating digit sum of N) = $1 - 0 + 3 - 7 + 6 = 3$
∴ $N = 10\,376$ *is not* exactly divisible by 11.

7 a Complete the equations.

$95\,359 = 11 \times \underline{\quad}$ $10\,376 = 11 \times \underline{\quad} + \underline{\quad}$

b Fill in the missing details in the following *justification* of the above rule.

Proof

Split up $N = \mathbf{95\,359}$ into separate powers of $\underline{\quad}$

$N = \mathbf{95\,359} = 9 \times 10^4 + \underline{\quad} \times 10^3 + \underline{\quad} \times 10^2 + \underline{\quad} \times 10^1 + 9 \times 10^0$

Then replace 10^4 by $(\mathbf{9999} + 1)$, 10^3 by $(\mathbf{1001} - 1)$, 10^2 by $(\mathbf{99} + 1)$, 10^1 by $(\mathbf{11} - 1)$, 10^0 by $(\mathbf{0} + 1)$.

$N = \mathbf{95\,359}$
$= \mathbf{9} \times (9999 + 1) + \mathbf{5} \times (1001 - 1) + \mathbf{3} \times (99 + 1) + \mathbf{5} \times (11 - 1) + \mathbf{9} \times (0 + 1)$
$= \mathbf{9} \times 9999 + \mathbf{5} \times 1001 + \mathbf{3} \times 99 + \mathbf{5} \times 11 + \mathbf{9} \times 0 + (\,\mathbf{9} - \mathbf{5} + \mathbf{3} - \mathbf{5} + \mathbf{9})$

$10000 - 1, 1000 + 1, 100 - 1, 10 + 1, 1 - 1$ are all exact multiples of $\underline{\quad}$ (by problem $\underline{\quad}$).

∴ $\mathbf{95\,359}$ is an exactly divisible by 11 *precisely if the alternating digit sum* $(\mathbf{9} - \mathbf{5} + \mathbf{3} - \mathbf{5} + \mathbf{9})$ is exactly divisible by 11.   **QED**

8 a *Without doing the division* decide which of these integers is an exact multiple of 11.

i 132	**iv** 1221	**vii** 9372	**x** 3729
ii 234	**v** 1331	**viii** 2739	**xi** 3927
iii 242	**vi** 286	**ix** 9327	**xii** 3972

b Check each of your claims in part **a** by carrying out the division.

9 a Choose any three-digit integer '*abc*'. Reverse the order of the digits and subtract, '*abc*' – '*cba*' = ___.
Take the answer '*def*'; reverse the order of the digits and add: '*def*' + '*fed*' = ___.
Write your final answer.

b Choose a second three-digit starting integer '*abc*', and repeat the same procedure.

c Choose a third three-digit starting integer '*abc*', and repeat the same procedure.

10 The key to understanding the surprising outcome in problem **9** lies in seeing why there are very few possibilities for the intermediate answer '*def*'. To get started repeat problem **4** in slow motion.

a i Without evaluating 853 – 358, explain why the remainder when 853 – 358 is divided by 9 is equal to '(remainder when 853 is divided by 9) – (remainder when 358 is divided by 9)'.

ii Without evaluating 853 – 358 use **C41** problem **5b** to explain why 853 – 358 must be exactly divisible by ___ (see problem **4** above).

iii What does this tell you about the intermediate answer '*def*' in problem **9**?

b i Look again at the rule for divisibility by 11 in problem **7** above. By imitating **C41** problem **5b** more carefully, improve this rule so that it tells you the value of the remainder on division by 11.

ii Use this improved rule to identify another factor of the intermediate answer '*def*' in problem **9**.
Conclude that there are exactly 10 possible positive values for the intermediate answer '*def*'.

iii Write these ten possible values of '*def*'. Then add each number in your list to its reverse '*fed*'.
What answer do you get each time?

E3   More word problems   NC

Tackling word problems is the simplest, and one of the most important, ways to learn to *use* elementary mathematics. Each problem is given in words, so you must

◎   read it carefully (from the beginning *to the end*)

◎   sort out what you have to do

◎   extract the information from the problem as stated, and then

◎   do the necessary calculation to get the required answer.

1   Kiri changed a £20 note into 10p and 50p coins. She had three times as many 10p coins as 50p coins.
How many of each kind did she have?

2   Adam is 8 kg heavier than Eve, and Cain is 4 kg heavier than Abel. The sum of the weights of the heaviest and the lightest persons is 2 kg less than the sum of the weights of the other two. The sum of all four weights is 402 kg.
How much does each person weigh?

3   'Give me 8 sheep and then we will have an equal number' said one shepherd to another.
'No, you give me 8 sheep and then I will have twice as many as you' replied the other shepherd.
How many sheep did each shepherd have to start with?

4   A father and son are out walking. The father's steps are 80 cm long, while the son's steps are 60 cm long. In the course of their walk, the son takes 5000 more steps than the father.
How far do they go?

5   *A, B, C, D, E* and *F* are six different towns in order along a winding road. The total distance from *A* to *F* is 101 miles, the distance from *B* to *E* is 78 miles, the distance from *A* to *D* is 83 miles and the distance from *C* to *F* is 42 miles.

   a   What is the distance from *C* to *D*?

   b   How many possible values are there for the distance from *B* to *C*?

6 a What is the largest amount of money less than £1 that I can have in standard British coins without being able to pay exactly 50p?

   b What is the largest amount of money I can have in standard British coins (excluding £2 coins) without being able to pay exactly £1?

7 A well is 20 m deep from the stone rim to the surface of the water. A snail starts at the surface of the water and climbs 4 m per day and then sleeps at night. While asleep, he slips back 2 m each night. How long does he take to reach the rim?

8 Alex has three loaves and Bob has five loaves. Charlie is hungry but has no food; however, he does have £8. Charlie agrees to pay his £8 to Alex and Bob if they agree to share the bread equally between the three of them. Alex and Bob agree.
   How should Charlie's £8 be divided between Alex and Bob?

9 A power company offers three sales packages, each with guaranteed savings: one saves 30% of current bills, the second saves 45% of current bills, while the third saves 25% of current bills. If all three packages could be combined, what total percentage could you save on your current bill?

10 (*The Abbot of Canterbury's Puzzle: AD 735–804*)
   One hundred bushels of corn were distributed among one hundred people in such a way that each man received three bushels, each woman received two bushels, and each child received half a bushel. Given that there were five times as many women as men, how many children were there?

E4 More angles

1 What is the sum of the four angles a, b, c, d in the diagram?

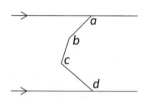

2 Find the unknown marked angle in each figure.

a
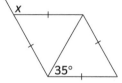

c
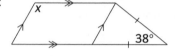

e
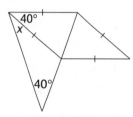

b
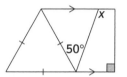

d
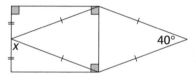

f
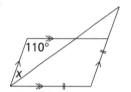

EXTENSION

3 *ABCDEFGH* is a regular octagon. How big is $\angle ADG$?

4 *ABCDEFGH* is a regular octagon. The diagonals *AC* and *BE* cross at *X*. How big is $\angle AXB$?

5 In triangle *PQR* the point *S* lies on the side *PQ* such that triangle *PRS* is equilateral and has half the area of triangle *PQR*. Find the size of $\angle PRQ$.

6 In the rectangle *ABCD*, $\angle ADB = 70°$. *P* lies on the side *AB* such that *AP* = *AD*, and *R* lies on *AD* produced such that *AR* = *AB*. *PR* and *BD* cross at *Z*. Calculate $\angle BZP$.

7 *ABCD* is a square. *M* is the mid-point of *BC* and *N* is the mid-point of *AD*. The circle with centre *N* and passing through *M* meets *CD* at *X*. Find $\angle NXM$.

8 In the parallelogram *ABCD* the point *M* lies on *AD*, and the point *N* lies on *BC* such that $\angle ABM = \frac{1}{3}\angle ABC$ and $\angle BAN = \frac{1}{3}\angle BAD$. *AN* and *BM* meet at *X*. How big is $\angle MXN$?

E5 More ratios

EXTENSION

1 **a** Which provides the bigger shares, 4 bars of chocolate shared between 9 people, or 5 bars shared between 11 people?

 b Which provides the bigger shares, $n - 1$ bars of chocolate shared between $2n - 1$ people, or n bars shared between $2n + 1$ people?

2 Divide £2.10 between three children in the ratio $9:4:1$.

3 Divide £108 between three people X, Y and Z so that Y has 5 times as much as Z, and X has half as much again as Y.

4 The sides of a triangle are in the ratio $1:1.5:2$. If the perimeter is 36 cm, find the lengths of the three sides.

5 Fill in the missing numbers in these *three-way* ratios.

 a $32:16:48 = 2:1:\_\_\_$

 b $36:\_\_\_:40 = \_\_\_:36:20$

 c $\_\_\_:60:36 = 39:\_\_\_:18$

6 Three boys, X, Y and Z, share a sum of money in the ratio $4:7:9$. What percentage of the total sum did Y receive?

7 X, Y and Z share some stamps in the ratio $2:3:5$.
 Z received 60 more stamps than X.
 Find the total number of stamps shared by the three boys.

8 Two numbers are such that their difference, their sum and their product are in the ratio $1:4:15$. What are the two numbers?

9 The sides of a triangle are in the ratio $2:3:4$. The shortest side has length 5 cm. Find the perimeter of the triangle.

10 Three men, A, B and C, agree to share the expense of a fishing expedition in the ratio $2:3:4$.
 A pays £25 for the hire of the boat, B pays £70 for meals and C pays £49 for travelling expenses.
 How much must A and C pay B to settle their agreed shares?

11 How many pears can I buy for £1.08 if seventy almonds cost the same as fifty chestnuts, forty eight chestnuts cost the same as one pomegranate, eighteen pomegranates cost the same as twenty eight lemons, ten lemons cost the same as twenty five pears, and one hundred and eight almonds cost 9 p?

E6 More HCFs and LCMs NC

You know about the *highest common factor* and the *least common multiple* of *two* integers.

If you are given *three* integers, their *highest common factor* has to be a factor of all three integers.

For example, $hcf(42, 105) = 21$, $hcf(105, 70) = 35$, $hcf(42, 70) = 14$
$\therefore hcf(42, 105, 70) = 7$
Similarly, $lcm(42, 105, 70) = 210$

Find the *hcf* and the *lcm* for each *triple* of integers.

1 $hcf(6, 10, 15) =$ $lcm(6, 10, 15) =$

2 $hcf(30, 42, 105) =$ $lcm(30, 42, 105) =$

3 $hcf(30, 105, 70) =$ $lcm(30, 105, 70) =$

4 $hcf(77, 91, 143) =$ $lcm(77, 91, 143) =$

5 $hcf(65, 143, 55) =$ $lcm(65, 143, 55) =$

6 $hcf(182, 715, 1001) =$ $lcm(182, 715, 1001) =$

7 $hcf(154, 385, 1014) =$ $lcm(154, 385, 1014) =$

8 Three local churches toll their bells at intervals of 8 s, 15 s and 9 s. If all three toll together at 8 am, when will they next ring exactly together?

9 Four wooden rods of lengths 140 cm, 238 cm, 168 cm and 210 cm are cut into shorter pieces that are all the same length. If no wood is left over, what is the smallest possible number of pieces?

10 A button manufacturer produces buttons in three colours, red, white and blue. They decide to package the buttons in packets, such that each packet contains buttons of only one colour, and all packets contain the same number of buttons – which should be as large as possible.
If they have 388 800 red buttons, 3 542 940 white buttons and 1 244 160 blue buttons, how many buttons should go in each packet so that none are left over?

E7 Number squares

1 Arrange the numbers 1, 2, 3, 4, 5, 6, 7, 8, 9 in the nine squares of a 3 by 3 table so that the three rows, the three columns, and the two main diagonals all have the same sum.

2 Arrange the numbers 2, 3, 4, 5, 6, 7, 8, 9, 10 in the nine squares of a 3 by 3 table so that the three rows, the three columns, and the two main diagonals all have the same sum.

3 Arrange the numbers 1, 3, 5, 7, 9, 11, 13, 15, 17 in the nine squares of a 3 by 3 table so that the three rows, the three columns, and the two main diagonals all have the same sum.

4 Arrange the numbers 2, 4, 6, 8, 10, 12, 14, 16, 18 in the nine squares of a 3 by 3 table so that the three rows, the three columns, and the two main diagonals all have the same sum.

5 Arrange the numbers 11, 22, 33, 44, 55, 66, 77, 88, 99 in the nine squares of a 3 by 3 table so that the three rows, the three columns, and the two main diagonals all have the same sum.

6 Arrange the numbers 1, 11, 21, 31, 41, 51, 61, 71, 81 in the nine squares of a 3 by 3 table so that the three rows, the three columns, and the two main diagonals all have the same sum.

The next problems are slightly different: you have to arrange n symbols in an n by n grid so that each row, each column (and, if possible, each diagonal) contains n different symbols.

7 a Arrange the numbers 1, 2, 3, 1, 2, 3, 1, 2, 3 in the nine squares of a 3 by 3 table so that each row and each column contains three different numbers.

b Prove that it is not possible to arrange the numbers 1, 2, 3, 1, 2, 3, 1, 2, 3 in the nine squares of a 3 by 3 table so that each row, each column *and each of the two diagonals* contains three different numbers.
(Suppose that such an arrangement were possible, with the top left corner containing x. Then the top right corner square must contain a *i**e*e** number y.

What can you say about the number that goes in the central square? And what does this tell you about the entry in the bottom left corner?)

8 Arrange the numbers 1, 2, 3, 4 in the squares of a 4 × 4 table so that the four rows, the four columns and the two main diagonals each contain four different numbers.

9 Complete this arrangement of the digits 1, 2, 3, 4 in the squares of a 4 × 4 table so that each of the four rows, the four columns and the two main diagonals contains four different digits.

10 Complete this arrangement of the digits 1, 2, 3, 4 in the squares of a 4 × 4 table so that each of the four rows, the four columns and the two main diagonals contains four different digits.
How many different solutions are there?
Justify your claim.

11 Complete this arrangement of the digits 1, 2, 3, 4 in the squares of a 4 × 4 table so that each of the four rows, the four columns and the two main diagonals contains four different digits.
How many different solutions are there?
Justify your claim.

E8 More prime factorisation

NC

EXTENSION

◎ $4 = 2 \times 2 = 2^2$, so the only factors of 4 are
$2^0 = 1$, $2^1 = 2$, $2^2 = 4$.
These factors give rise to the factor diagram on the right.

◎ $8 = 2 \times 2 \times 2 = 2^3$, so the factors of 8 are
$2^0 = 1$, $2^1 = 2$, $2^2 = 4$, $2^3 = 8$.
These factors give rise to the factor diagram on the right.

◎ $6 = 2 \times 3$, so the only factors of 6 are
$2^0 \times 3^0 = 1$, $2^0 \times 3^1 = 3$,
$2^1 \times 3^0 = 2$, $2^1 \times 3^1 = 6$.
These factors give rise to the factor diagram on the right.

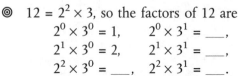

◎ $12 = 2^2 \times 3$, so the factors of 12 are
$2^0 \times 3^0 = 1$, $2^0 \times 3^1 = \_\_\_$,
$2^1 \times 3^0 = 2$, $2^1 \times 3^1 = \_\_\_$,
$2^2 \times 3^0 = \_\_\_$, $2^2 \times 3^1 = \_\_\_$.
These factors give rise to the factor diagram on the right.

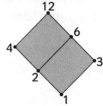

Problem 0

> **0** Write each integer as a product of prime powers; hence write down all its factors. Draw the factor diagram. (Use a ruler and make sure your diagrams capture the structure of each number.)
>
> **a** $9 = \_\_\_ \times \_\_\_ = \_\_\_^2$ ∴ the factors of 9 are $\_\_\_^0$, $\_\_\_^1$, $\_\_\_^2$.
>
> **b** $10 = \_\_\_ \times \_\_\_$
> ∴ the factors of 10 are $\_\_\_^0 \times \_\_\_$, $\_\_\_^0 \times \_\_\_$
> $\_\_\_^1 \times \_\_\_$, $\_\_\_^1 \times \_\_\_$.
>
> **c** $18 = \_\_\_ \times \_\_\_$ ∴ the factors of 18 are $\_\_\_$

1 Write each integer as a product of prime powers; hence write down all its factors. Draw its factor diagram. Make sure your diagrams capture the structure of each number.

a 14	**e** 27	**i** 91	**m** 44
b 21	**f** 35	**j** 49	**n** 63
c 28	**g** 75	**k** 98	
d 50	**h** 77	**l** 25	

2 When factorised as a product of prime numbers 6, 10, 14, 21, 35, 77, 91 all have 'the same structure', since each is equal to the product of *two different primes*:

$$6 = 2 \times 3, \quad 10 = 2 \times 5, \quad 14 = 2 \times 7, \text{ etc.}$$

One consequence of having the same structure is that all of these integers have *the same number of factors*.

a List the factors of 6, 10, 14, 21, 35, 77, 91 in the same *systematic* way used for 6 in the text at the beginning of the section, to show they each have exactly 2×2 factors.

$$6: 2^0 \times 3^0, \quad 2^0 \times 3^1; \quad 2^1 \times 3^0, \quad 2^1 \times 3^1$$
10:                 ;
14:                 ;

b Look at the factor diagrams for 6, 10, 14, 21, 35, 77, 91. Describe the shape of each diagram. How do these diagrams show that each of these integers must have exactly 2×2 factors?

c Find all integers ≤ 50 which have the same 'factor structure' as 6.

3 When factorised as a product of prime numbers 12, 18, and 28 all have the same structure, since each is equal to the *square of one prime* times *a different prime*:

$$12 = 2^2 \times 3 \quad 18 = 3^2 \times 2 \quad 28 = 2^2 \times 7.$$

One consequence of having the same structure is that all three integers have *the same number of factors*.

a List the factors of 18 and 28 in the same *systematic* way used for 12 in the text at the beginning of the section, to show they each have exactly 2×3 factors.

$$12: 2^0 \times 3^0, 2^0 \times 3^1; \quad 2^1 \times 3^0, 2^1 \times 3^1; \quad 2^2 \times 3^0, 2^2 \times 3^1$$
18:         ;   ;
28:         ;   ;

b Factorise 50 and 98 as products of prime powers. List the factors of 50 and 98 in the same *systematic* way used for 12 in the text at the beginning of the section, to show they each have exactly 2×3 factors.

$$12: 2^0 \times 3^0, 2^0 \times 3^1; \quad 2^1 \times 3^0, 2^1 \times 3^1; \quad 2^2 \times 3^0, 2^2 \times 3^1$$
50:         ;   ;
98:         ;   ;

c Look at the factor diagrams for 12, 18, 28, 50 and 98. Describe the shape of each diagram. How do these diagrams show that each of these integers must have exactly 2×3 factors?

d Find another integer ≤ 30 which has the same factor structure as 12, 18, 28, 50 and 98.

e Find all integers ≤ 100 which have the same factor structure as 12.

4 a Go through the list of integers in problem 1 and group them into just *four different families*, where all the integers in each family have the same factor structure.

   b For each of your four families, decide exactly how many factors the integers with that factor structure have. Use the factor diagrams to explain why this number of factors is what it is.

5 8 and 6 can both be factorised as a product of two factors in two different ways:

$$8 = 1 \times 8 = 2 \times 4; \quad 6 = 1 \times 6 = 2 \times 3.$$

However, the prime factorisation of these two integers is quite different:

$$8 = 2^3; \quad 6 = 2 \times 3.$$

   a In Section C3 you produced the following list of integers N for which there are *two* different rectangles, each made of N unit squares:

   4, 6, 8, 9, 10, 14, 27, 49, 91.

   Split the integers in this list into three separate groups, where the integers in each group have the same factor diagrams (and hence the same factor structure).

   b In Section C3 you produced the following list of integers N for which there are *three* different rectangles, each made of N unit squares:

   12, 16, 18, 20, 32, 81.

   Expand this list to include *all* such integers ≤ 50 (there are four others).

   Split the integers in the complete list into three separate groups, where the integers in each group have the same factor diagrams (and hence the same factor structure).

   c List all integers $N \leq 100$ for which there are four different rectangles, each made of N unit squares. Identify three distinct families (with one family including a single integer).

6 Factorise each of the following integers as a product of primes. Then draw a beautiful factor diagram for that integer.
   In each case decide whether the integer is in one of the four families you identified in problem 4a, or whether it belongs to some new family.

a 52	f 24	k 135	p 200
b 99	g 9	l 72	q 42
c 39	h 40	m 30	r 32
d 125	i 121	n 144	s 70
e 54	j 143	o 108	t 96

In problem **1** you used the prime factorisation of various integers to draw their factor diagrams.

In problem **4** you used this information to group together integers that have the same factor structure: in particular you discovered that all the integers in problem **1** have the same factor structure as one of the four integers
$$(*) \quad 14 = 2 \times 7, \quad 12 = 3 \times 2^2, \quad 49 = 7^2, \quad 27 = 3^3.$$

In problem **3** you saw that any integer having the same factor structure as $12 = 2^2 \times 3$ (say) must have the same number of factors as 12.

> For example, $175 = 7 \times 5^2$
> $\therefore$ any factor of 175 has the form $7^a \times 5^b$,
> where $a = 0$ or 1, and $b = 0$, 1 or 2.
> (If $a = 0$ and $b = 0$, then we get the factor $7^0 \times 5^0 = 1$.
> If $a = 1$ and $b = 2$, then we get the factor $7^1 \times 5^2 = 175$. And so on.)
> There are 2 choices for a and 3 choices for b
> $\therefore$ there are 2×3 possible factors.

For the same reason, any integer with the same factor structure as
$$12 = 2^2 \times 3, \quad \text{or} \quad 175 = 7 \times 5^2$$
also has exactly 2×3 factors.

7 Factorise each of the following integers as a product of primes. Use this prime factorisation to decide how many factors the integer must have. Draw its factor diagram as elegantly as you can. Finally decide whether the integer has the same structure as one of the four integers in (∗) above, or whether it belongs to a new family.

a 16	g 32	m 108	s 144
b 48	h 81	n 250	t 42
c 169	i 96	o 135	u 70
d 56	j 72	p 500	
e 48	k 343	q 1000	
f 125	l 200	r 30	

E9 Crossnumbers

A *crossnumber* is like a crossword, but with digits in place of letters.
One digit goes in each small square, and no answer begins with a '0'.

1 Find all possible solutions to this crossnumber, and prove that you
have found them all.

CLUES

Across
1. Multiple of 25
3. Square

Down
1. Multiple of 3
2. Three times a prime

2 Find all possible solutions to this crossnumber, and prove that you
have found them all.

CLUES

Across
1. Square of a prime
4. Prime
5. Square

Down
1. Square of another prime
2. Square
3. Prime

3 Find all possible solutions to this crossnumber, and prove that you
have found them all.

CLUES

Across
1. Even multiple of 9
3. Square
4. $31 \times \sqrt{2D}$

Down
1. Cube
2. Square
3. Cube

4 Find all possible solutions to this crossnumber, and prove that you
have found them all.

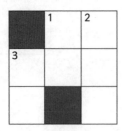

CLUES

Across
1. Prime number
3. Square of 3D

Down
1. Prime number
2. Square of 1D
3. Square root of 3A

5 Find all possible solutions to this crossnumber, and prove that you have found them all.

1	2	■
3		4
5		

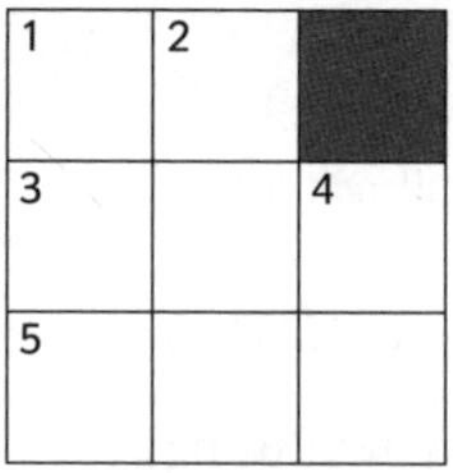

CLUES

Across	Down
1. Factor of 5A	1. Square
3. Even	2. Cube + 1
5. Square of 4D	4. Less than 100

6 Find all possible solutions to this crossnumber, and prove that you have found them all.

1	2	■
3		
4		■

CLUES

Across	Down
1. Square	1. Square
3. Square	2. Square
4. Square	

E10   1089 and all that

'It was the element of mystery and surprise that put this result into a different league from the work we were doing in school.'

(David Acheson, *1089 and All That*)

Positive integers are usually written in our *base 10* numeral system using the digits 0–9 and powers of 10, for example,

$$2735_{base\ 10} = 2 \times 10^3 + 7 \times 10^2 + 3 \times 10^1 + 5 \times 10^0$$

Integers can also be written in other bases – such as

 a *base 2*, using the digits 0–1 and powers of 2, for example,

$$2735_{base\ 10} = 2048 + 512 + 128 + 32 + 8 + 4 + 2 + 1$$
$$= 1 \times 2^{11} + 1 \times 2^9 + 1 \times 2^7 + 1 \times 2^5 + 1 \times 2^3$$
$$+ 1 \times 2^2 + 1 \times 2^1 + 1 \times 2^0$$
$$= 101010101111_{base\ 2}$$

or

 b *base 9*, using the digits 0–8 and powers of 9, for example,

$$2735_{base\ 10} = 3 \times 729 + 6 \times 81 + 6 \times 9 + 8$$
$$= 3 \times 9^3 + 6 \times 9^2 + 6 \times 9^1 + 8 \times 9^0$$
$$= 3668_{base\ 9}$$

In *Book Alpha* (Section **E10**) you practised addition and subtraction in bases other than 10. In this book (Section **E2**, problems **9** and **10**) you had a glimpse of the '1089' puzzle. This section looks at variations on this puzzle in *base 10* and in other bases.

1 a Choose any two digit integer '*ab*'$_{base\ 10}$, with $a > b$.
Reverse the order of the digits and subtract: '*ab*' – '*ba*' = ___.

Interpret the answer as a two-digit integer in *base 10* (possibly with first digit equal to 0); reverse the order of the digits and add: '*cd*' + '*dc*' = ___.
Write down your final answer.

```
  a b
– b a
─────
  c d

  c d
– d c
─────
  * *
─────
```

b Choose a second two-digit starting integer '*ab*', with $a > b$ and repeat the same procedure.

c How many possible final answers are there? Can you see why?

2 a Use **C39** problem **5** to explain why '*ab*' – '*ba*' in problem **1** must be exactly divisible by ___. What does this tell you about the intermediate answer '*cd*' in problem **1**? What does this tell you about '*dc*' – and hence about the final answer '*cd*' + '*dc*'?

b Look again at the rule for the remainder when dividing by 11 in **E2** problem **10b**. Use this rule to identify another factor of the final answer '*cd*' + '*dc*'. Conclude that there is just one possibility for the final answer.

3 a Choose any two digit integer '*ab*'$_{base\ 9}$, with $a > b$.
Reverse the order of the digits and subtract: '*ab*' – '*ba*' = ___.

$$\begin{array}{r} a\ b \\ -\,b\ a \\ \hline c\ d \\ \hline \end{array}$$

Interpret the answer as a two-digit integer in *base 9*;
reverse the order of the digits and add: '*cd*' + '*dc*' = ___.
Write down your final answer.

$$\begin{array}{r} c\ d \\ -\,d\ c \\ \hline *\ * \\ \hline \end{array}$$

b Choose a second two-digit starting integer '*ab*', with $a > b$
and repeat the same procedure.

c How many possible final answers are there? Can you see why?

4 a Choose any two digit integer '*ab*'$_{base\ 8}$, with $a > b$.
Reverse the order of the digits and subtract: '*ab*' – '*ba*' = ___.

$$\begin{array}{r} a\ b \\ -\,b\ a \\ \hline c\ d \\ \hline \end{array}$$

Interpret the answer as a two-digit integer in *base 8*;
reverse the order of the digits and add: '*cd*' + '*dc*' = ___.
Write down your final answer.

$$\begin{array}{r} c\ d \\ -\,d\ c \\ \hline *\ * \\ \hline \end{array}$$

b Choose a second two-digit starting integer '*ab*' with $a > b$
and repeat the same procedure.

c How many possible final answers are there? Can you see why?

5 a Choose any 3-digit integer '*abc*'$_{base\ 9}$, with $a \neq c$.
Reverse the order of the digits ('*cba*') and subtract the
smaller 3-digit integer from the larger.
Carry out the subtraction in *base 9*.

$$\begin{array}{r} a\ b\ c \\ -\,c\ b\ a \\ \hline d\ e\ f \\ \hline \end{array}$$

Treat the result as a 3-digit integer in *base 9*; reverse the order
of the digits and add (in *base 9*).
Write down the 4-digit answer.

$$\begin{array}{r} d\ e\ f \\ +\,f\ e\ d \\ \hline *\ *\ *\ * \\ \hline \end{array}$$

b Multiply the 4-digit answer to part **a** by 8. What do you notice
about the answer?

c Calculate $8 \times (11_{base\ 9})^2$.

6 a Choose any 3-digit integer '*abc*'$_{base\ 8}$, with $a \neq c$.
Reverse the order of the digits ('*cba*') and subtract the smaller
3-digit integer from the larger. Carry out the subtraction wholly
in *base 8*. Treat the result as a 3-digit integer in *base 8*; reverse
the order of the digits and add (in *base 8*).
Write down the 4-digit answer.

b Multiply the 4-digit answer to part **a** by 7. What do you notice
about the answer?

c Calculate $7 \times (11_{base\ 8})^2$.

E11 Integer problems NC

1 a Find a four-digit integer such that the product of the two middle digits is 28; the product of the two outer digits is 40; the hundreds digit is as much less than the tens digit as the thousands digit is less than the units digit.

   b Find a four-digit integer such that the product of the two middle digits is 12; the product of the two outer digits is 21; the hundreds digit is as much less than the tens digit as the thousands digit is less than the units digit.

   c Add your answers to parts **a** and **b**. What do you notice?

2 a How many positive integers ≤ 100 can be written as the product of two even integers?

   b How many positive integers ≤ 500 can be written as the product of two perfect squares?

3 a Evaluate $2^6 \times 5^5$.

   b When the number $3^4 \times 4^5 \times 5^6$ is written out in full (in *base 10*), how many zeros will there be on the end?

4 5! is shorthand for $5 \times 4 \times 3 \times 2 \times 1$.

   a Work out the exact value of 4!. What is the units digit?

   b Work out the exact value of 5!. What is the units digit?

   c Work out the exact value of 6!. What is the units digit? What is the tens digit?

   d If you were to calculate the exact value of 7!, how many zeros would there be on the end? What about 8! ? What about 9! ? What about 10! ?

   e If you were to calculate the exact value of 15!, how many zeros would there be on the end? What about 20! ? What about 25! ?

5 a I roll one ordinary dice. What is the probability that the score is even?

   b I roll two ordinary dice. What is the probability that the total is even?

   c I roll two ordinary dice. What is the probability that the total is a prime number?

6 Find the sizes of all possible integer-sided rectangles whose area is numerically equal to their perimeter.

7 £1 buys 40 stamps chosen from 1 p, 4 p, 12 p. How many are there of each kind?

8 a Which is biggest: 33^3, 3^{33}, or 3^{3^3}? Justify your answer (no calculators!).

   b Which is biggest: 44^4, 4^{44}, or 4^{4^4}? Justify your answer (no calculators!).

9 a Without working out $hcf(111, 11\,111)$, explain why
         $$hcf(111, 11\,111) = hcf(111, 11).$$

   b Find the highest common factor of
         111 111   and   1 111 111 111 111 111

10 The integer m lies between 10 and 99 (inclusive); n is obtained by reversing the digits of m. The difference between m and n is one-eleventh of their sum. Find m and n.

11 The three-digit square number 400 becomes a one-digit square number when its digits are reversed. How many three-digit squares are there which become *three-digit* squares when their digits are reversed?

12 a Find three prime numbers that between them use the digits 1, 2, 3, 4, 5, 6 once each.

   b How many different solutions are there to part a?

13 $2^0 = 1$, so $2^0 + 2^3 = 1 + 8 = 9 = 3^2$. Find two other (unequal) powers of 2 whose sum is a perfect square. How many such pairs are there?

14 You can use matches to make regular polygons as long as you use the same number of matches for each edge of a given polygon. What can you say about the number of matches in a matchbox if, for each pair of polygons in the following list, it is possible to make *both* polygons at the same time using up *all* the matches in the box each time?

   equilateral triangle, square, regular pentagon, regular hexagon

15 a 6 is called a *perfect* number, because when you add up all its factors you get exactly double the number you started with:

$$1 + 2 + 3 + 6 = 12$$

(Alternatively, the sum of all the **proper** factors of 6, that is, those factors that are strictly less than 6, is exactly equal to 6.) Find the next smallest perfect number after 6.

b 8 is called a *deficient* number, because when you add up all its factors that are strictly less than 8 you get a number *smaller than* the number you started with:

$$1 + 2 + 4 = 7$$

How many deficient numbers are there < 50?

c 12 is called an *abundant* number, because when you add up all its factors that are strictly less than 12 you get a number *larger than* the number you started with:

$$1 + 2 + 3 + 4 + 6 = 16$$

  i What is the next smallest abundant number after 12?

  ii Find the first six abundant numbers.

d i Calculate the sum of all the **proper** factors of $m = 220$. Let n stand for the answer.

  ii Calculate the sum of all the proper factors of n.

  Any pair of integers like $m = 220$ and $n = \underline{\quad}$ are called *amicable* numbers.

  You might like to check that $m = 1184$ and $n = \underline{\quad}$ is another such pair.

E12 More word sums

In a word sum each letter stands for one of the digits 0–9. Different letters stand for different digits, and each letter stands for the same digit each time it occurs. None of the integers in the sum starts with a '0'.

Your job is to work out which digits the letters could stand for (using logic rather than guesswork).

Some of the word sums in this section have no solutions (in which case you have to explain why no solution is possible); some have just one solution (in which case you should try to find that solution and prove that it is the only one); some have several solutions (in which case you should look for a logical approach which guarantees that you will find them all; this is sometimes rather hard).

1 One of these two sums has no solutions. Which one is it?

```
a     T  H  I  S         b              A  N  D
   +  W  O  N' T                     T  H  I  S
      W  O  R  K                        O  N  E
                              +  D  O  E  S  N' T
                                 E  I  T  H  E  R
```

2 Find a solution, or prove that there are no solutions, for each of these word sums. Where a solution exists, you might like to try to find *all* possible solutions.

```
a     W  O  R  K      b     S  U  M  S      c        T  R  Y
   +  W  O  R  K         +  S  U  M  S               T  R  Y
      H  A  P  P  Y         T  H  I  N  K         +  T  R  Y
                                                    G  O  A  L
```

3 Find a solution, or prove that there are no solutions, for each of these word sums. Where a solution exists, you might like to try to find *all* possible solutions.

```
a     S  E  V  E  N      b           T  E  N      c     S  E  V  E  N
            S  I  X                  T  E  N            T  H  R  E  E
   +  S  E  V  E  N         +  F  O  R  T  Y         +        T  W  O
      T  W  E  N  T  Y         S  I  X  T  Y            T  W  E  L  V  E
```

4   Find the solution for each of these classic word sums, and prove each solution is unique.

a
```
  H O C U S
+ P O C U S
P R E S T O
```

b
```
  C R O S S
+ R O A D S
D A N G E R
```

c
```
    S C A N
+ T H E S E
D I G I T S
```

5   The first of these has one solution, the second three solutions, the third four solutions! Find them.

a
```
        A
  M E R R Y
    X M A S
T U R K E Y
```

b
```
     X M A S
A) H A P P Y
```

c
```
     X M A S
A) M E R R Y
```

6   In this word sum, I, M, O, N, T and P stand for different digits.
```
  I ' M
+ O N
T O P
```

   a   Which digits are uniquely determined?
       Explain your answer.

   b   How many solutions are there with P = 0?

   c   By considering each possible value of P in turn, show that
       the word sum has 78 solutions.

E13 100% Proof

In Section **T20** *Types of triangle* you noticed that

In any triangle ABC

if a (= BC) is the longest side, then A(= $\angle BAC$) is the largest angle

and

if A(= $\angle BAC$) is the largest angle, then a (= BC) is the longest side.

Without a proof, this observation about all triangles remains a guess based on a few experiments. You may think it sounds so logical that no proof is needed. But it is all too easy to be seduced by the obvious-sounding poetry of

'if ____ is *longest*, then ____ must be *largest*, and

if ____ is *largest*, then ____ must be *longest*'.

In mathematics, what sounds 'logical', or 'reasonable' to the uncritical observer is often plain wrong. One aim of this section is for you to see that a proof is needed (problem 2) and to provide a simple proof (problem 3).

But first we look at a quite different rule which many pupils think is obvious, but which is in fact false.

1 In Sections T22 and C37 you worked hard at mastering the art of adding and subtracting fractions. The basic strategy you should now have mastered is the following:

To add fractions $\frac{a}{b}$, $\frac{c}{d}$ with *different denominators*

◎ the first step is always to rewrite both fractions so that they have the *same denominator*

$$\frac{a}{b} = \frac{(a \times d)}{(b \times d)} = \frac{ad}{bd} \qquad \frac{c}{d} = \frac{(c \times b)}{(d \times b)} = \frac{bc}{bd}$$

◎ once the denominators are the same, addition is simply a matter of adding the *numerators*

$$\frac{a}{b} + \frac{c}{d} = \frac{ad}{bd} + \frac{bc}{bd} = \frac{(ad + bc)}{bd}$$

Nevertheless, those who think they can make up their own rules often think it is simpler to add numerators and denominators separately, and so write (incorrectly):

$$\frac{a}{b} \, '+' \, \frac{c}{d} = \frac{(a + c)}{(b + d)}.$$

This is so *wrong* that it gives the *wrong answer* for almost all choices of *a, b, c, d*!

a i Simplify $\dfrac{1}{2} + \dfrac{(-1)}{2} =$

 ii Simplify $\dfrac{(1 + (-1))}{(2 + 2)} =$

b i Simplify $\dfrac{1}{2} + \dfrac{2}{4} =$

 ii Simplify $\dfrac{(1 + 2)}{(2 + 4)} =$

c i Simplify $\dfrac{9}{6} + \dfrac{(-1)}{2} =$

 ii Simplify $\dfrac{(9 + (-1))}{(6 + 2)} =$

d i Simplify $\dfrac{2}{3} + \dfrac{(-1)}{2} =$

 ii Simplify $\dfrac{(2 + (-1))}{(3 + 2)} =$

e Try to give a complete description of *all* pairs of fractions $\dfrac{a}{b}$ and $\dfrac{c}{d}$ which satisfy $\dfrac{a}{b} + \dfrac{c}{d} = \dfrac{(a + c)}{(b + d)}$.

In the Section **C11** *Calculating angles* B you proved the *Exterior angle theorem*:
'Given any triangle ABC, if you produce AC to the point D, then the exterior angle at C is equal to the sum of the two interior opposite angles at A and at B.

$$\angle BCD = 180° - \angle BCA \quad \text{(angles on a straight line)}$$
$$= \angle CAB + \angle CBA \quad \text{(angles in a triangle).'}$$

In problem **3** on the next page this result is used to prove beyond all doubt that the longest side in any triangle is always the side opposite the largest angle.

But first problem **2** gives you a chance to see that the same result is *false* for pentagons.

2 Draw an equilateral triangle XYZ.

a Mark the point T on the side XY such that $XT = 2 \times TY$.
Mark the point W on the side XZ such that $XW = 2 \times WZ$.
Let U be the point on the side YZ where the perpendicular from T meets YZ.
Let V be the point on the side YZ where the perpendicular from W meets YZ.
Explain why $YU = ZV = \frac{1}{6}YZ$.

b i Which are the longest sides in the pentagon TUVWX?

ii Calculate the size in degrees of the five angles in the pentagon TUVWX.
$T = \_\_°$ $U = \_\_°$ $V = \_\_°$ $W = \_\_°$ $X = \_\_°$
Which are the largest angles?

iii Which is the side 'opposite' angle T?
Which is the side 'opposite' angle W?

Problem 2 shows that 'longest side' and the 'largest angle' do not always go together; in the pentagon TUVWX in problem 2, the three *longest* sides are opposite the three *smallest* angles! This should convince you that the result for triangles cannot just be taken on trust, but requires a proper proof.

3 Fill in the gaps in the following proof that

In any *triangle ABC* the *longest* side is always opposite the *largest* angle.

Claim

If $AC > BC$, then $\angle ABC > \angle BAC$, so the longest side is opposite the largest angle.

Proof

Since $AC > BC$, we can find a point D on the side AC such that $CD = CB$.

Then $\triangle CDB$ is isosceles	(since $CD = \_\_$).
$\therefore \angle CDB = \angle C\_\_$	(base angles of an i*o**e*e* triangle are equal)
$\therefore \angle CAB < \angle DAB + \angle DBA$	(since $\angle CAB$ and $\angle DAB$ are the *a*e a***e)
$\_\_ = \angle CDB$	(*Exterior angle theorem* for $\triangle D\_\_$)
$\_\_ = \angle CBD$	(base angles of isosceles $\triangle C\_\_$)
$\_\_ < \angle CBA$	
$\therefore \angle CAB$ is *less than* $\angle CBA$.	**QED**